GONE FOR A BURTON

Memoirs from
a
Great British Heritage

By

BOB RICKETTS

Pen Press Publishers Ltd

First published in Great Britain by
Pen Press Publishers Ltd
25, Eastern Place
Brighton
BN2 1GJ

ISBN 1-905203-42-X

Printed and bound in the UK by Cpod, Trowbridge, Wiltshire

A catalogue record of this book is available from
the British Library

Cover design by Jacqueline Abromeit

ABOUT THE AUTHOR

 Bob Ricketts spent all his working life in beer, which did no harm to his desire to extract enjoyment from daily existence at work, and to share this pleasure with all and sundry, no matter what their calling.

A fortunate education, followed by continual accidents of being in the right place at the right time, allowed him to do most of the front line jobs in the great British beer heritage of the 20th century, with its largely unheralded quality of service to the community.

During those years, he served as President of the Institute of Brewing, and on the Executive of the European Brewing Convention; and instead of being thrown on the scrap heap on retirement, became involved in helping the major professional brewing qualifications into a new millennium.

He peaked as Managing Director of Bass Brewing, producing a quarter of the UK's beer output from 11 breweries, just as the battles were beginning to be lost against those who eventually destroyed everything that he felt he had tried so hard to represent.

He is married, with an ample supply of grandchildren, and alternates a quiet rural life near Burton-on-Trent with the sunshine in South West France.

It is said that advancing age develops the capacity to recall, with increasing clarity, things that never happened.

I plead with the reader to reserve this generalization for others, whilst I dedicate this book to the inspirational characters that make up this true account of life in the corporate world.

Over nearly half a century, they consistently demonstrated how the timeless incompatibilities between human nature and professional conduct can still be used in the pursuit of excellence and career satisfaction. Except, of course, when they cannot.

However, between them all, one can assemble all the qualities in the human being that make a working life worth living.

CONTENTS

Introduction

INTRODUCTION

The Great British Heritage referred to in the title was, like many other heritages, ingrained in the culture of the nation and, therefore, for a long time unrecognised and taken for granted. That is, until political influences and vociferous minorities started interfering. Among the hardest things to keep at bay were the effects of those who thought they knew better than the majority what was good for them.

The heritage in question was the successful commitment of the breweries, throughout most of the 20th century, to provide cheap beer, in agreeable social surroundings, in every locality in the land. Every village had its 'local' as a hub of the community, serviced by the local breweries that usually had complete control over the presentation of the pub and its beer to the public. This included the landlords and landladies themselves, many of whom would become pillars of local society. Additionally, active civil disciplines on alcohol-related misbehaviour existed, non-adherence to which threatened the future of both publican and the pub licence, together with the reputation of the brewery.

The framework of this book is how the brewers faced up to half a century of external pressures threatening this culture, with characteristic wisdom, humour and folly. They were rewarded with the irrecoverable collapse of the major brewing companies into foreign hands in the 1990s. This also involved the break-up of the single-company (vertically-integrated) chain from brewery to bar, that was essential for sustaining the historic commitment to the communities.

The core of the book is the involvement of the loyal staff in this changing environment, in a way that should apply to employment in any business. When combined with the sheer pleasure of the brewer's product – the best social lubricant that can be enjoyed, in moderation, over a long period of time – we create a huge fraternity of fellow souls. They are those who have to work under all manner of adversity, and who often relieve their stress by socialising within an arm's length of a bar. This book is for them.

We will travel through all the normal management irritants such as stupid regulations, bosses, subordinates, trades unions, financiers, accountants, consultants and personnel officers. To this must be added consumer pressure groups, together with government oppressions through taxation, investigations and controls, as additional burdens to test the humour and best intentions of any manager, let alone a poor brewer. It is these things that combine to cause the inevitable clash between human nature and good management practice, requiring a sideways look from time to time to restore sanity. Such comment, advice and techniques are offered in copious amounts.

*

Let us start with the Middle Ages. Although beer has been around for 5000 years, it was the monks who made most use of its three magical qualities. Firstly, it is incapable of supporting human disease organisms, hence the availability of pollution-free drink so important in those days. Secondly, it is nutritious and an important source of vitamins. Thirdly, of course, is its use as a social lubricant, hence its hospitality value.

A daily ration in a monastery has been recorded as eight pints of weak ale and a pint or two of strong ale; this must have been quite sufficient to justify their reputation as jolly monks. If there were any dregs left after that, the monks were obviously capable of nourishing both the bodies and the souls of visiting pilgrims at the same time, under the same roof. This is a fine early example of effective multi-tasking.

Another advantage to the celibate monks was that they presumably never discovered the one side effect of extended beer drinking, namely Brewer's Droop. This is a temporary phenomenon accepted as self-inflicted by the cognoscenti, in preference to their next-best form of entertainment. I could name a number of my brewers who might well have been the originator of the saying 'sex is all right, but not quite like the real thing'.

Strangely, the brewers in the 1950s were not short on fathering (mothering was not an option available to brewers in those days). In one brewery in Burton-on-Trent they produced 14 children in a five-year period, 13 being girls. Such statistical significance inevitably raised intense debate about which of the special qualities of Burton beer was responsible.

Although it seemed that I had to move to Burton to father a daughter, following a stream of sons, I did not involve myself in analysing such statistical significances, as I had already done my lessons on that subject. To me, statistics are like bikinis - what they reveal is suggestive, what they conceal is vital.

It had been discovered in the late 18th century that Burton beers could be transported across the country and readily sold at a premium, as a result of their quality being far superior to that of locally-produced beers. In the 100 years that it then took to discover the reason and keep the secret of this phenomenon, the fame of Burton had spread across the world, which may explain why it features so strongly in this book

The young brewers already mentioned were the first post-Second World War generation, slowly taking over from the ageing and infirm who had held the fort during the war, with no opportunities, facilities or incentives to break from archaic traditions and attitudes. This is where the book really starts, in the 1950s.

*

This is not a technically-minded book, so it may be helpful to explain a few words and phrases, albeit common knowledge to experienced beer and pub enthusiasts.

Beer: All types of fermented brewery products derived principally from malted barley (malt), including ales and lagers.

Ale: Traditional British beer available in cask (*cask conditioned* in the pub cellar before sale, referred to by enthusiasts totally incorrectly as *real ale*), or ready to drink from keg, can or bottle.

Lager: Continental style beer, normally paler in colour, with a higher gas (carbon dioxide) content than ale and drunk at a lower temperature. Available only in ready-to-drink containers.

Draught beer: Any beer served through a tap at the bar.

Wort: The sugary liquid obtained from the brewing ingredients before the yeast is added to ferment it into beer. (Pronounced 'wert').

Original Gravity (OG): The specific gravity ('strength') of the *wort,* on which excise duty was paid from 1880 to 1993. Thereafter, duty has been paid on the alcohol content of the finished beer.

CHAPTER 1

JOINING THE 20th CENTURY

In the early 1950s, a standard beer cost one shilling and four pence a pint, and petrol was approaching four shillings a gallon. The inflation chart tells us that, at the turn of the millennium, things are 15 times more expensive than 50 years before. Therefore we should reasonably expect to be paying £1 for a pint of beer today and £3 for a gallon of petrol - not a bad shot for petrol, but the fact that it is difficult to find beer at under £2 per pint demands an explanation for this obvious nail in the coffin for the future of the industry.

The high price of beer today is not due to disproportionate increases in excise duty; in fact, duty was 50 per cent of the retail price in the 1950s, and nothing like that now, even if including VAT. So the true situation is even worse than it seems.

How this came about, in association with the complete destruction of the stable structure of the beer and pub industry, mostly into foreign and financiers' hands, is a sorry tale surrounding the people who had to live, work and cope with it.

To make matters worse for these loyal and devoted people, the net result has been far more serious than any previous criticism of corporate behaviour in the alcohol business: to be in agreement with this, one has only to observe the lack of control by young people concerning alcohol abuse.

The systematic process of amalgamation of brewers during the first half of the 20th century had reduced the number of licensed breweries from 11000 to around 500, owned by only some 300 companies. This process of survival of the fittest had caused little public concern because the quality of the pub had improved massively over the years, without any reduction in the availability of cheap beer in small communities. The 'local' still meant exactly what it said.

It could be said that the structure of the industry had settled down into a set pattern, the vast majority with their own 'tied' pubs, with opportunities to compete in the 'free' trade, notably clubs, off-licences and any other privately-owned business with a licence to sell alcoholic drinks.

The exceptions were the brewers of national brands established over 100 years or more, taking advantage of their unique qualities to become 'must stock' products in every outlet around the country. The obvious ones were Guinness stout, and the Bass and Worthington pale ales of Burton-on-Trent; the former remains today a unique universal product, the latter less so since the secret ingredients of Burton water became known in late Victorian times.

Today, despite all the changes of the last 50 years, Burton just about remains the true centre of brewing, albeit largely foreign-owned producing around 15 per cent of the whole UK output. Even so, this could not have been without the big national-brand brewers in the town having entered the pub acquisition field as well, to secure enough 'tied' trade essential for financial stability in the changing world.

*

During the 1950s, distinctions between social classes had begun to set new boundaries, following relatively improved living standards through full employment during the Second World War, together with new efforts by the post-war Labour Government to introduce universal benefits, most notably the National Health Service.

This was the era of the 'working man's pint', and with increasing public attention to the Cost of Living Index of which beer became an important constituent, beer was inevitably to become a political football for government, trades unions and the lot of the working class (whatever that really meant). At that time, the working class was said to be able to afford a television set but not a car, while the middle class could afford a car but not a television set: it should not have needed much in the way of change to blur that boundary. But it was not to be for decades; there were too many factors and vested interests in play deliberately maintaining a strict division between the two.

The upper class had been represented in the beer world by 'the beerage', a phenomenon among proprietors of the largest and most powerful breweries, who were acquiring hereditary peerages up to the 1920s, for reasons that did not always seem to have much to do with beer. That was, of course, an era when wealthy businessmen stood for parliament (where the breweries were well represented, not necessarily on the Conservative benches), mainly because there was little for the directors to do other than to raise the status of their empires, thus enabling them to pursue their own private or public agendas.

In the brewery, the head brewer was God, it being accepted that the process was so mysterious and little understood that only he, after decades of brewing experience, was capable of commanding such a fickle process. Thus the directors were not particularly welcome in the brewery anyway, other than in their paternalistic role.

By the 1950s the beerage had mostly disappeared from the scene, presumably having to be intent on preserving their heritage against public opinion and the swingeing income tax and death duties of the time. Only the few with genuine ability

3

and a desire to control the destiny of their own companies remained, together with sons and heirs who would henceforth have to advance themselves more by merit than through their blood line, as the brewing business steadily increased its professionalism.

The autumn of 1956 marked the end of Britain's undisputed influence in the world through its bloody nose at Suez, allowing anyone then joining the business world to be increasingly free, if so desired, of arrogant aspirations of empire or nepotism. Despite the apparent stability of the structure of significantly-sized regional and local brewers, as well as the two or three large brewers of national brands, things were not going to be able to remain in that cosy state for very long.

*

"Meet Ricketts. He's come down from Cambridge with a degree in chemistry, so the first thing you have to do is to teach him some chemistry". This was my introduction to my research manager by Professor Sir Ian Heilbron, F.R.S. (Fellow of the Royal Society), director of the Brewing Industry Research Foundation, on the very first morning of my very first job.

Others might have been wholly deflated, infuriated or even sharp-witted enough to fling back a suitable riposte to such a challenge to one's pride, let alone to that of one's alma mater. However, having been released only the previous week from two years of honourable service in Her Majesty's Armed Forces, I was shocked that such gratuitous insults could occur in civilian life as well.

I reacted exactly as I had learnt from bitter experience, deciding there and then that I would start a file of useful things to remember; not only for my own benefit, but perhaps for others should I ever be in a position of management leadership at some time in the future.

Note to file of useful things to remember:
When faced with a deliberately degrading insult from your superior:
1. Look him straight in the eye.
2. Adopt a facial expression half way between a total blank and mild incredulity.
3. On no account operate mouth before brain.
4. Obtain any required relief by writing obscene messages on the roof of your mouth with your tongue.

Despite this rather poor start in the first minute of my career, I was not diverted from making use of a privileged education in science by actually *working* in the field of science. It seemed wrong to think of any other kind of job after the efforts and resources that the taxpayer had provided for me.

This worthy altruism did not extend beyond accepting the highest offer available from the wealth of graduate scientist vacancies available in those days. In 1956, the going rate for a fresh graduate scientist was £650 p.a., so even a few increments on that, usually in multiples of £50, made a disproportionate difference to one's initial standard of living.

In my case this represented the minimum ability to support a wife and nascent family: a good enough reason for entering the world of beer, altruism slightly to the wind, accidentally falling on one's feet at the precise time when brewing was hardly out of the dark ages of technology, but ready to take its quantum leap into the 20th century.

It had been in 1951, five years earlier, that this research foundation had been established by the entire British brewing industry, being the first common effort to advance scientific understanding of the brewing process. Before that, the larger breweries had their own scientific facilities; in fact, at one time there were at least four Fellows of the Royal Society working in Burton-on-Trent alone (the 'mecca' of brewing - possibly the original oxymoron) during the early 1900s. Why, then, was the industry so technically backward 50 years later?

The answer lay in the continuing god-like status of the brewer, exposing his delusions of adequacy, with the freedom as to whether he made use of his scientists or not. However, it was extremely fashionable at that time for the upper classes to be interested in scientific matters, so extensive laboratory facilities were built and manned in many breweries, but often primarily as showpieces for important visitors. Certainly, one Fellow of the Royal Society in a Burton brewery was given the brief to research into anything he liked, so long as he never came anywhere near the beer.

In 1920 the head brewer of Whitbread in London, famous for its laboratory facilities at which Louis Pasteur had worked at one time, had declared of his scientists that he 'favoured the principle of any improvements suggested, but was grieved and hurt by any implication that the historic methods and usages were less than perfect'. What more elegant phrasing could summarize both the state of brewing and the underlying resistance to change.

*

Note to file: It must be a good idea to have a stock of useful phrases that say 'yes', meaning 'no'. Or, at best, to be able to say both 'yes' and 'no' without contradicting yourself. If you have any doubts about this ability, just think of your MP.

Twenty years later, these conditions must have barely changed when, following the discovery of penicillin by Alexander Fleming, the Second World War created an instant massive demand for this wonder antibiotic. Being the first major drug that required production by a fermentation technique, the brewing industry was approached as possibly the preferred source of expertise for mass-producing the penicillin, rather than the pharmaceutical industry, whose skills at that time lay firmly established in the chemical synthesis of drugs and purifying natural products.

It would appear that the big breweries, despite their wealth of scientific knowledge of fermentation, at least in their laboratories, did not rise to the occasion. So the opportunity of a lifetime, if not centuries, was permanently lost, as the pharmaceutical boffins quickly taught themselves all that was necessary to know about fermentation technology.

This left the brewing companies to continue in their old fashioned way, using those brewers ineligible to go to war, thus delivering a thoroughly backward industry into the hands of keen young men returning from the war, anxious to make their mark in that brave new world.

When the Brewing Industry Research Foundation opened in 1951, it soon became a focus of discovery and excellence. Although intent on basic research into the nature of brewing, it seeded rather more extensive practical technological ideas than was perhaps originally envisaged, for here was knowledge to be exploited commercially by brewery technicians. What was more, this could be both around and over the head of the traditional head brewer, because it was the latter's bosses who were funding the research.

The year 1956 was a perfect time to join such an organisation. Five years in, teething problems had been resolved, and stable motivated staff were beginning to turn out stunning innovatory ways of improving those 'perfect historic methods and usages' of 1920. And what a wonderful place it was to work in - an original prototype of the modern 'research park'; a country estate with manor house set above sweeping lawns, gardens and trees in open countryside. It was reached by winding lanes concealing pretty little Surrey villages, yet within easy reach of London and the major supporters and users of the foundation.

With Sir Ian Heilbron to inspire the young into the field of research, having acquired his F.R.S. for work on the development of penicillin (totally unrelated to the previous reference to the drug), and bringing his top scientists with him from that university so vastly superior to Cambridge, who would ever want to leave such an idyllic place and existence?

One of the most important projects concerned the nature of cloudiness in beer after it had been bottled and pasteurized, the detailed cause and composition of which was then unknown. With luck and experience, it had been sometimes possible to keep the beer clear for only six weeks or so, which is why all the national beer brands were sent in bulk to distant breweries for local bottling and distribution to their own pubs, to be consumed before the beer started to deteriorate.

Compared to the present day, the variations in quality were enormous, and wholly unsuitable for modern retailing in shops and supermarkets, that now demand shelf lives of up to 12 months. Precisely how this quality became achievable can be illustrated by *one* of the ways in which research arrives at the solution to a problem, in this case the 'eureka' method of research.

One of the young scientists was delegated to find new types of powdered materials which might help to separate the various components that were thought to cause cloudiness in beer. Quite accidentally, he found an otherwise inert material (a powdered type of nylon) that would strongly adsorb one of the ingredients in the beer, which was then confirmed to be the essential one necessary to stop the other ingredients combining to form these hazy particles. Eureka! - an instant solution to one of the major commercial problems of beer quality, *and* without having to add anything to the beer.

The rush from the senior scientists to get their names on the patent (those, of course, who considered that they had had an important advisory role in the discovery) was so great that, in passing, they forgot to include the name of the actual discoverer.

Note to file: The vultures are everywhere. Even among those who must project intellectual honesty as an essential prerequisite to their work.

What happened next was exactly what seems to occur with almost all British inventions, including those of far more national and international importance than this particular discovery:

1. An offer is received from an overseas manufacturer of one of the less effective next-best processes, to buy the rights of the patent.

2. The offer is proudly, but politely refused.

3. The British manufacturer and supplier of the vital product loses interest, because of 'not enough immediate commercial potential'.

4. A foreign establishment develops and modifies the invention to the point of being able to get round the patent, re-patents it and then goes into business.

5. The original patentees retain their career brownie points, whilst the actual owners of the original patent (in this case the British brewers) have to pay royalties on the modified foreign process.

That course of events is another form of research, called the 'me too' method. As can be seen, it is highly cost-effective developing other people's ideas and discoveries.

The influence of the professor dominated other parts of the work of the foundation. It was time for the 10-year revision of his own personal project, named after him; The Heilbron Dictionary of Organic Compounds, six tomes naming the prime characteristics of every single organic compound known to man. Staff from the foundation was recruited to do this massive revision as an extra-mural activity outside working hours.

One evening I was working in the foundation library on this project, when a hand landed on my shoulder from behind and the professor asked me what I was coming across of interest at that moment. I showed him a page of his dictionary coincidentally full of organic compounds that he, and only he had discovered and characterized in the 1930s. Operating mouth before brain, I told him that a recent revival of interest in these compounds had proved his research findings to be totally wrong.

With the greatest kindness, he congratulated me on discovering one of the key essentials of a career in research.

"Take a tip from me, young man," he concluded, "in the field of discovery it doesn't matter if you are wrong, so long as you are first!"

I went home that evening turning this remarkable philosophy over in my mind, quite sure that there was a flaw in it somewhere. Suddenly realising the peril, that night I sent up a short prayer: 'Please God, if ever I need leading-edge surgery, don't let the surgeon be of that persuasion.' It was some time later that I decided to feel a lot more comfortable with a slightly modified approach to life:

Note to file: In the field of discovery, it doesn't matter if you are *second*, so long as you are *right*! Synonym: always include some 'me too' research in your armoury of commercial research and development projects. If you have any doubts about the value of this, think of Bill Gates.

It was not long before the charismatic professor retired, to be replaced by his deputy Dr Arthur Cook, another F.R.S., who had trailed Sir Ian Heilbron during his working life. He was the last man that I encountered who had deliberately sought his scientific education in Germany, reputed in the 1920s to be the source of all scientific excellence and discovery, presumably as a result of the high count of Nobel Prize winners emanating from there. This extraordinary point of view lasted even beyond the Second World War, when, in 1948, I was forced to study German as soon as I had selected sciences as my Higher Certificate subjects (the A-levels of those days).

The school had impressed on us that the only worthwhile scientific literature was written in German, and to be proficient in that language was the only way to a successful career in science. Unsurprisingly, I was somewhat linguistically challenged, having been brought up in that particular part of southern England (aka Suburbiton). This is where the school maps are reputed to be printed with the Arctic Circle going through Watford, the trains terminating at Crewe, and Hadrian's Wall holding back the relentless advance of the tundra; and where, if a foreigner can not understand you, all you have to do is to shout.

In the end, after two years of grinding study, I acquired 1 per cent in the examination. My teacher rubbed this achievement in even further by informing me that no examiner had ever given 0 per cent, because he would lose his one shilling and nine pence marking fee. My only consolation came from a classmate who, despite being fluent in German, achieved only 40 per cent; which only went to say something about our teacher too. Or was this the start of the collapse of confidence in the whole examination system that we all know and complain about today, 50 years later?

Following this ghastly failure, I can recall neither incident nor adverse effect of any kind whatsoever on the quality of my science or my career, through failure to be able to read a German scientific paper or text book. This has never surprised me; after all, it had been in Germany that the factory manager of an equivalent of ICI decided to break up a huge pile of artificial fertiliser, set solid through exposure to damp weather conditions, with the judicious use of quarry explosives.

They never confirmed the exact death toll, after a large part of the town had been laid flat. It is a pity that the Darwin award (made annually for the most spectacularly stupid action, where the perpetrator's death thereby protects the human gene pool) had not yet been invented.

Note to file: Always judge people, organizations, even nations by their actions, not their words. If you have any doubts about this, just think of the world's worst dictators.

Such sentiments did nothing to dilute respect for Dr Cook's science, but where he excelled in matters academic and intellectual, he found himself a bit short on the management skills so necessary to hold together a collection of ill-disciplined young scientists, and at the same time to be able to deal with the beer barons wanting to see value from their investment in the foundation.

His pet Rolls Royce in the forecourt kept him comfortably remote from the hoi polloi, who had to park their bangers at some distance, suitably screened from the eyes of those who needed to be impressed by the presentation of the foundation to the outside world. Being resident on the site, occasional discussions were held in his antique-laden living room, mainly to have admired the ultimate in television sets of the day, neatly plumbed into an exquisite Louis XV commode.

Control of his personnel inevitably became his major bugbear. Here was a bachelor with little experience outside academia, and with no management advice or assistance to fall back on. When some of the staff started being, let us say, a little liberal in the use of their holiday allowance, it fell to him to lay down the law in front of a full gathering.

"You are reminded of your employment conditions whereby you have to seek authority and reserve in advance your holiday periods," he announced. "This is not happening. Some of you are taking days off without any notice, and I know why; you are getting up, drawing back the curtains, seeing a beautiful day before you, and saying to your wife 'let's have it off'."

Note to file: To command respect from your underlings, you must keep up with modern terminology and jargon. If you have any doubts about this, just think of some of our judges.

At the time of his reign, things were changing in other ways. The industry was beginning to recognize the enormous commercial value of the foundation's output, but some breweries were finding that their own staff were not up to the standard required to implement effectively these research findings.

What could be more natural than to employ foundation staff to do just that? Thus began an exodus of some of the best brains, at doubled salaries or more, which the new director seemed to take as a personal insult, rather than seeing how stimulating and beneficial to the industry this, in fact, was.

It was many years later that a deliberate policy of reciprocal employment and interchange was introduced, which led to the foundation's move to a great international reputation. Back in 1959, however, such management creativity was hard to find, so Dr Cook took the situation into hand and issued an edict that, in future, no member of staff would be allowed to visit any brewery, thereby theoretically halting the outflow of talent. Inevitably, precisely the opposite happened; how was anyone to make their name in brewing if they were never allowed to even see a brewery? Sadly, it was time to move on.

*

My first venture into the real world of making beer was to join a supplier to the industry, and coming into contact with not only all the brewers in the country, but also all the suppliers and all the scientists working therein. Nothing could have been a better introduction to this unique world; unique because at least half of all the materials supplied to breweries, and half of all plant and equipment used for brewing is absolutely specific to that industry, thus creating a tight circle of mutually dependent businesses dedicated to beer excellence.

It took little time to discover that the other special characteristic of beer, namely that of being by far and away the best and most popular social lubricant, had created circles of close friendship, among all those committed to the profitable enjoyment of good beer.

Each 'unit' of the beer-making business, the brewers, the scientists, the suppliers of materials and equipment (Allied Traders) and the brewery owners, had its own association in which its members pursued their own specific interests. In 1960, I experienced the Incorporated Brewers' Guild fighting for the status and employment conditions of brewers, the

13

Institute of Brewing advancing the cause of science in brewing, the Allied Brewery Traders Association representing collectively the interests of the suppliers, and the Brewers Society dealing with all matters of public and governmental interest. Their interests exist today, but in highly modified formats and objectives appropriate to the changing times.

Such was the overlap of these interests that many individuals belonged legitimately to two or even more of these organizations. So everyone benefited from each other's interests: they attended each other's lectures and meetings (in pubs naturally), dinners (in licensed hotels), social functions (wherever there was free beer), and they discussed business and exchanged grape vine gossip over pub lunches and in the brewery sample store. The net result was that everyone knew pretty well exactly who was doing and thinking what, in an atmosphere of the considerable warmth and trust caused by the natural gravitation to an arm's reach of a bar counter.

In 1960, I started working for a stereotypical down-to-earth Lancashire businessman, whose father had established an industrial detergent business. Aimed mainly at the dairy industry, he had introduced the then outrageous concept of washing milk bottles and churns (no tankers in those days) with a chemical cleaning agent. Being a pharmacist by trade, he knew well the non-existent risks of a dilute solution of his detergent mixture, but to win over the fears of the poorly educated dairy managers of that time, he had a quantity of the powdered chemicals compressed into small cubes, which he would eat in front of these prospective customers.

Note to file: Success in business is all about individuality and commitment, but make sure first that it is not going to kill you.

It was his son who sought to expand this business into breweries, and it was to him that I became grateful for the introduction to the hard end of getting business; and in later years he won my admiration by becoming national chairman of the Allied Brewery Traders Association.

14

This was despite his propensity for gold bangles and a gaudy Rolls Royce as his business expanded under his leadership, an early example of the changing times requiring considerable getting used to by the ultra-traditional 'old-money' brigade among the suppliers and brewery directors.

*

The late 1950s represented the centre of another brewery takeover frenzy, initiated by a Canadian brewer, Eddie Taylor, who decided to convert the United Kingdom to the delights of drinking his Carling Black Label lager. Lager had been popular in Scotland for almost 100 years, but was barely 1 per cent of beer sales in England and Wales.

With seemingly no market research of the British way of doing things - surely, if you want to launch a product, all you have to do is to buy a factory, a marketeer and a sales force - he bought a brewery, produced his lager, and signally failed to make the planned impression on the market. It was unfortunate that he had bought one of the very few breweries that owned only a handful of pubs, thus prohibiting access to any, let alone enough, 'tied' outlets to establish his brand before attempting a national launch.

His solution to this problem was to buy every brewery that would sell to him, which he set about with a will. Other brewing companies recognized the threat, not least because there were only a limited number of companies (300) in existence, and therefore any of their own plans for expansion at some time in the future suddenly became a matter of urgent review. Thus began a scramble for companies and their pubs, resulting, in a matter of a decade or so, in the massive concentration of the industry, which might never have happened but for the failure of a foreigner to understand the workings of his market.

Note to file: It seems to be a good idea to know what you are doing before you do it.

As a technical representative visiting breweries during the height of this activity, it was obvious to me that many of the brewing plants taken over would not be wanted, and I was struck by a direct correlation between closures and the reluctance of their brewers to purchase cleaning materials. This did my business no harm, but brought home the appallingly backward state of the industry at that time.

It is not, in fact, strictly necessary to maintain a scrupulously clean brewery. This is because of the remarkable property of beer to inhibit growth of organisms that are dangerous to humans, thus allowing considerable scope for interpretation of hygiene requirements in the brewery.

But the risks were great. There were plenty of organisms lying in wait around a brewery that would render beer less than palatable, ranging from plain cloudiness to off-flavours such as vinegar, parsnip, rotten egg, rancid butter, and even a bug that will turn beer into a semi-liquid suppurating floppy jelly that pours from a bottle like a length of rope. These were all fairly common problems in those days, but rarely did they initiate urgent attention to the cleaning routines, which the traditional head brewer had been perfectly content with.

On one occasion, a keen young trainee brewer, sent by the head brewer of a very large brewery to supervise the annual de-scaling of the beer pipes, found his finger thick with dirt after wiping it inside a cleaned pipe. Showing it to the head brewer, he was told, "Young man, one day you will learn to recognize that there are two types of dirt, clean dirt and dirty dirt. What you have on your finger is clean dirt. Now go back and keep the men on the job."

Note to file: Think of life as one long process of picking up pearls of wisdom.

It could be said that the massive concentration of the industry in the 1960s was, in fact, a good thing, if only that it got rid of the complacency over extreme variations in the quality of beer.

Certainly today there is no scope whatever to present anything but consistently excellent quality, produced in immaculately clean plants, although the handling of cask conditioned beers in the pub cellar by the landlord will forever create quality variations for the consumer.

It took some time for the public to come to terms with this newly-found attention to excellence. As late as 1975, I visited a large pub in the City of London, following conversion of the cellar from cask to 'tank' beer, delivered in perfect condition straight from the brewery into a sterile stainless steel tank in the cellar. I overheard one customer, who was looking astounded at his sparkling pint, say to his companion, "Good God, Joe, what on earth have they done to the beer?"

"I think they did something to the cellar", he replied, "but never mind; knowing the landlord, it will be back to normal in no time!"

Having been thoroughly indoctrinated with the need for a revolution in cleaning techniques in the brewery, capable of generating a worthwhile career in its own right, I thought it opportune to enquire of the boss whether he would like to tempt me with a directorship, to raise the status of such a huge project. I realized afterwards that I had not chosen the best moment; his solicitor had just reminded him that a board meeting (of him and his wife, the sole directors) was long overdue, and what was the problem, since surely he could have held it at any time, in bed?

Some earthy folk outside the legal or brewing profession have to be excused from not seeing the funny side of such imperative matters, so it was not surprising that my career decided to take an alternative route.

Note to file: Beware the possible effects of others' senses of humour on your own prospects. And your own for that matter.

My next adventure was with an engineering company in Burton-on-Trent, the very heart of British brewing. In the 1960s many people described Burton as difficult to forget, but well worth the effort; at least nobody knew where it was or how to get to it, without studying a map.

At one time it had over 30 breweries, arising from the unique quality and unlimited availability of superb brewing water, obtainable simply by digging a hole in the ground to one side of the River Trent where lay the gravels of the ancient river course. Needless to say, it was monks who first made good use of this remarkable phenomenon.

The discovery that Burton beer was of highest quality, even after a long journey, caused a major change to the geography of England. Its network of waterways was expanded and centred on Burton, for carrying beer to Hull for the Russian Court, then to Liverpool for export to India and other imperial activities out east.

The London Midland Railway was deliberately routed through Burton to carry beer all over the country, thus establishing the town as the premier national source of the highest quality pale ales (the type of beer most suited to Burton water). In true paternalistic style, a Bass was a prime instigator and founder of the first Railwaymen's trade union.

It was inevitable that the town would grow on the back of its brewing industry, rather than vice versa. The patronage of the beerage provided the town with the status of a borough, plus all manner of exotically-designed public buildings (John Betjeman described the town hall as a fine example of a Victorian railway station), whilst public use of the town centre competed with 30 private brewery railway crossings and 17 miles of track.

The rail links were needed to feed the huge breweries in the centre of town with coal, malt, hops and washed casks, then to deliver the casks of beer back to the main railway line.

It was not a question of the breweries being in the town centre, it was the town centre that was in the middle of the breweries. Not only the town, but more importantly the inhabitants and their livelihoods, had become steeped in this paternalistic brewing tradition for generations.

It is astonishing that this state of affairs lasted until about 1970, by which time conversion to road transport was being matched by efficient concentration of the brewing operations on to much smaller sites. It seemed that almost overnight the brewers gave the town back to its people, leaving vast unwanted areas in the centre. Today, the town enjoys extensive shopping facilities with central parking, whilst the few breweries remaining produce more beer than ever before - around 15 per cent of the whole UK output. And it still enjoys its borough status and air of geographical isolation; a survey conducted in the streets of the town revealed that 90 per cent of inhabitants could not give directions on how to get to the county town of Stafford!

Back in 1963, the engineering company that I joined benefited greatly from being in Burton. The owner self-styled himself as being from the black sheep side of one of the important Burton brewing families, which helped to provide a constant flow of local orders for brewing equipment as the financial base for more adventurous engineering projects.

It was the time when automatic control of production processes was the 'in' subject of interest to engineers; but, being years away from microprocessors and other modern electronic gadgetry, the most advanced control equipment of the day was operated by compressed air. So new was this exciting development, that the boss had built an automatic brewery on the premises, for two reasons it seemed; firstly, to show off this superior technology to his customer base (the whole world of brewing), and secondly to impress his hunting, shooting, fishing friends by supplying them with copious quantities of free beer.

In fact, the whole world of business in Burton in those days seemed to be through personal contact; in the field of brewing, in particular, it was even more vital not to give any form of offence to anyone of importance, for fear of being ostracized.

The little brewery turned out three barrels of beer per week in the cause of the automatic control project. There always seemed to be a firkin (a nine-gallon cask) left over after satiating the requirements of his county set, so the managing director decided to sell it to one of the free trade clubs in the town, and found the police club a willing buyer.

Within a fortnight he had received a letter from his second-cousin-first-removed chairman of one of the local breweries, pointing out that he was stealing his trade (of more than a million barrels a year) to the tune of one firkin a week, and unless he ceased forthwith he would receive no more orders for brewing equipment

Note to file: It pays to know your place in the family hierarchy.

This little brewery experienced the same delights as the major breweries in dealing with Her Majesty's Customs and Excise, and all their ludicrous control systems for double or triple-checking every part of the brewing process. This could only be explained by an overriding assumption by the excise that the sole ambition of a brewer was to cheat them.

Bearing in mind that these excise officers were interchangeable with jobs at ports or any other type of control of dutiable goods, it was not unreasonable, I suppose, that their dealings with the gentlemen of the brewing industry should merit an unusual level of untrustworthiness. I discovered later how right they had been, at least in the past.

Meantime, because this brewery hardly merited a resident excise officer, the first excise check was the obligation to give at least two days' notice, in writing, of the date and hour at which it was intended to brew, *by post*, to the resident officer in the big brewery 50 yards down the road. Since all the brews were 'experimental' in the sense of testing new automatic systems, no-one ever knew exactly when the plant would be properly set up for brewing.

We often had to give notice of intent to brew at every single hour of every day of the week, and enter these (by law) in the excise book provided. Every one of these then had to be cancelled, hour by hour, until all the controls were set up for the brew to start. The amount of excise duty on this weekly three-barrel brew might have amounted to about £30 in those days, which must have made us the highest expense-ratio, time-consuming, paper wasting system for collection of excise duty devised.

Whilst the Excise might have lacked gentlemanly qualities, contracts for fabricating and installing brewing plant, particularly those involving considerable design work, had necessarily to be as much by gentlemen's agreement and mutual trust as by firm pricing. In those days, breweries were such complex rabbit warrens of buildings in which to fit new plant, and brewers anyway were well known to change their minds on design halfway through an installation, that it was physically impossible to cost accurately every detail of a job.

To keep the job going apace, business was therefore often done on retrospective pricing of variations from the original quotation, in the knowledge that both parties were gentlemen. The contractor had the additional potential penalty of being subject to ostracism in the event of trying to pull a fast one on the customer.

At some time or another, someone always comes along to spoil such thoroughly sensible and mutually satisfying ways of doing business and it always *seems* to be an accountant. One year we had successfully quoted for a new brewery, representing two thirds of our annual turnover. Progress payments in advance were being made, as was normal practice, and the job was threequarters finished at the end of our financial year, when a new auditor, totally green to the brewing industry, arrived to check the books. He worriedly tackled the managing director about the apparent absence of an order for the brewery.

"No problem," he replied, "There's the quotation in front of you, and we shook hands on it."

"May I remind you that a limited company cannot shake hands," snapped the auditor. "If you cannot produce an order, I will be unable to approve your accounts."

In fear and trembling at having to challenge the customer's integrity by asking for an order, he rang the chief engineer and tried to explain the difficult position he was in with his auditor.

"Don't worry a bit about it, John," the engineer had replied, "I'll put one in the post to you tonight."

The following morning there arrived an envelope, within which was one of those grubby requisition slips that maintenance craftsmen use to draw nuts and bolts (or whatever) from engineer's stores. This one had the usual array of oily fingerprints on it, and beneath the heading 'please supply' was entered 'one brewery'.

Note to file: To succeed in business you must obviously have the right relationship with accountants. Or is it true that *every* accountant is a condom on the spearhead of progress?

Orders for whole breweries were pretty rare, therefore icing on the cake, to be appreciated at every possible opportunity. An excellent project had been completed in West Africa, and the customer, one of the largest brewing companies, had requested a repeat quotation for installation in South East Asia. For the first time, the workshop was so booked up that it would not be possible to meet the customer's time scale, but at the same time it would be equally critical to refuse such a customer a quotation, for fear of losing him for ever.

The solution was not particularly innovative, namely to quote such a high price that there would be no chance whatever of getting the order, but unfortunately (or fortunately depending on how one looks at it) the quotation was accepted.

On those sorts of occasions one does not spare effort to

complete the project up to the highest standards. Nearly 30 years later, when on an international tour as president of the Institute of Brewing, I was taken to the brewery to see their recent massive redevelopment; and there, in the middle of their new facilities, was that original brewing plant perfectly preserved as a museum exhibit, to show visitors the height of brewing technology in the 1960s. Satisfaction all round for everyone.

The only other event of significance allied to this profitable project was that the company went bust. These two things did not seem to me quite to add up, but by that time I had already been tempted away on to the scientific staff of one of the biggest breweries in Burton.

The strange Burton rituals of the day had been scrupulously followed, involving instructions to apply for the job through a certain box number in a certain newspaper on a certain day, so that no-one could be accused of poaching from another Burton-based beer-related organization.

This proved to be the great opportunity to direct my experience to the 'hands on' end of creating beer excellence. Understanding the mysteries of accountancy in profitable business would have to wait.

CHAPTER 2

LIFE WITHOUT SERVICE FUNCTIONS

The scrabble for breweries and their pubs continued through the 1960s. As the number of smaller ones available for purchase declined, and Eddie Taylor's empire assumed larger proportions, attention was being paid to the fate of the larger brewing operations. Of special significance was the Midlands merger of the Bass empire in Burton, big on national distribution but low on pubs, with Mitchells and Butlers, big on regional pubs and the beer trade in the industrial Midlands. This was considered a life-saver for both parties: Bass was not going to be able to stop the decline in national distribution to smaller breweries as they reduced in numbers and improved their own beer quality. Mitchells and Butlers did not have the resources to expand geographically without a merger.

Another feature of the times had been the first entrepreneurial attack on the brewing industry from outside. In 1959, Charles Clore of Sears Holdings, who had the reputation of being a 'financial marauder' (the expression 'asset stripper' was only just coming into fashion) tried to acquire Watney Mann's 3,900 pubs into his property development empire. The takeover bid was unsuccessful because of a rise in the brewery's share price beyond Clore's bidding limit, but it provided yet another incentive to further major mergers as a defence against such assaults in the future.

Whitbread had a reputation for being more paternalistic, philanthropic and cultural than other southern companies – it was said that it was easy to spot a Whitbread man in the street from his clothes and his bearing – and had taken a different view on all these mergers. Instead of joining the rush in the late 1950s, it expanded by taking minority 'umbrella' shareholdings in 20 quoted brewing companies to protect them from the takeover mania of the times. It allowed them their continued independence in return for reciprocal beer trading agreements. However, any gentlemanly approach to the merger maelstrom was not to last beyond the 1960s, when the really big guns were to start coming out.

*

I stepped across my new career threshold in early January 1966, as a proud employee of what I knew was the greatest brewing company in the land. This was not quite as momentous as it sounds, because Bass' brewing operations were so spread across the town and surrounding countryside that it would have been possible to have chosen from as many as 100 thresholds to have crossed unnoticed.

The brewing was in the hands of a thoroughly modern production director, the best leader that I have met. I shall refer to him as Sir, because that was the only form of address that he was prepared to accept from his minions. Sir had been driving the brewing operation out of post-war doldrums and historic complacency, but at a pace that allowed for yesterday's head brewers to make their dignified exits into retirement. In other words, a particular skill of his was to appreciate which parts of the traditional techniques and historic paternalism were continuing to give value to the business, whilst preparing for the forefront of new technology and production efficiency.

Legend has it that Sir and another brewer had come and sold themselves to the directors (they must have, because they would never have been approached or advertised for). So ambitious were each of them to be the one to lead the company truly into the 20th century, they came to a mutual agreement that not even one of the largest breweries in the land was big enough for both of them. So they tossed a coin for who would find his future elsewhere. The loser (or was he the winner?) departed, and made a highly successful career in a delightful part of the Emerald Isle.

It is always difficult to discover the jealously-guarded secrets of leaders, but they invariably cause speculative interest and usually subsequent admiration. Sir's invaliding out of the wartime Air Force, shortly after starting flying school, was inevitably assumed to be as a result of a spectacular daredevil prang; but others were imagining how equally appropriate it would have been if he had fallen off a table during a mess party, whilst demonstrating leadership skills to his equally inebriated peers.

And what was it that had inspired Sir to dictate in the 1960s that, in future, all his brewers must be graduates? He, himself, was fully capable of holding his own on technical matters, with an educational background as speculative as that of certain of our Prime Ministers. Meantime, he had issued slide rules to the brewers (and himself), to simplify the essential mathematics required of brewers for precision brewing.

Note to file: Always keep yourself and your employees up to date with the latest management tools.

Another great strength, which Sir rigidly applied to himself as well as his staff, was to insist on learning everything necessary about a process or practice before letting oneself loose on it, whether as advisor or manager. I was to be despatched to do three months of practical shift brewing, before being allowed to take up my job of applying scientific skills to it.

This involved the problem of being taught by those employees, from whom one then had immediately to command their respect. This is a style of training which is best carried out away from one's future working territory, preferably in another company, when all one's blunders can conveniently be lost in the mists of time and distance. But this was not to be for me, as I recorded my textbook tip:

Note to file: The secret of commanding respect from others is to be seen to respect their territory, with due humility towards their own skills and ways of doing things, in exactly the same way that you will expect this from them.

There were three breweries, and I was to work in the New Brewery, which had recently celebrated its centenary. The 'mind your head' signs were written in Polish (a relic from the war); the brewers had a private bathroom; there was an unreliable lift with a small compartment marked 'for emergency use only' (containing not a phone but a toilet roll); entries in the leather-bound brewing books had transferred from quill to fountain pen (but ball-points were strictly forbidden); and the steam trains chugging around the private railway system had been converted to diesel. Modernity was storming in.

By the 1960s, each train had been limited to a maximum length, in recognition of increasing numbers of impatient car drivers needing a reasonable chance of navigating the company's 30 level crossings spread throughout the town. Nobody had calculated that shorter trains meant more trains in direct proportion; and that every time the gates were being closed and reopened, the time during which the train was not actually crossing remained the same. To work out the net result of this restriction does not need a slide rule - but at least the town centre experienced neither bank robberies nor smash-and-grab raids.

All these sops to modernity did not go very far towards compensating for the unremitting acres of red Victorian brick, sprawling both sideways and upwards, within which was contained the traditional equipment unique to Burton brewing. It is not unfair to say that, inside these imposing but ugly temples, there lay an almost perfect time warp.

However, before being let loose in the brewery, I had to be introduced to the local geography. The whole Bass operation covered literally square miles. Each well supplying the unique Burton brewing water was surrounded by a minimum quarter-mile of open farmland, to prevent any conceivable contamination from human activity. Since these wells were open holes in the ground, which had produced limitless quantities of water of identical composition for more than 100 years, their protection was a sound strategy, if one ignored the omnipresent cow pats nearby. This one brewing company had around 30 wells and bores, the most important of which were named Nile Well, Cairo Well and similar names appropriate to imperialist glories of the past. Connection of these wells to the breweries in the town was through miles of underground pipes, laid in those times and with many still in use today.

A measure of the extraordinary nature of the brewing water supply in Burton occurred at the peak of the great drought of 1976, when the level of a single well 10 feet in diameter, pumping 25000 gallons an hour continuously, dropped only two feet below normal.

A visit to the company's maltings revealed the Scutari site, via Dixie, which somewhat tested my knowledge of past imperial glories, but everywhere were even bigger piles of Victorian brick, necessary for the conversion of finest barley into the grains of malt used for brewing. I was privileged to be under the wing of the head maltster himself, to be shown some of the art and mystery of the process, which had become thoroughly outdated whilst I was at the Brewing Research Foundation nearly ten years before. Another time warp.

However, the head maltster still thought himself the epitome of modernity. Predecessors had been allowed the privilege of a horse and carriage to take them on their daily tours of all the maltings scattered around the town, but this had been discarded as being somewhat dated. He was now seen and admired on his daily journey ensconced in a chauffeur-driven London taxi.

Note to file: In positions of high authority, style is all important.

I then had to delve into the scale of the other services that the brewery seemed to need - engineers, plumbers, electricians, joiners, coopers, cask washing, ale stores, hop stores, to name but a few. Many, of course, were disappearing as obsolescence started to take its toll, but this only made those remaining seem even more remote from each other, scattered all over the town but connected by rail.

For instance, only a few years before, a new brewer had to report to the tailors and cloggers department, to be measured up for his white coat. The clogs, however, had been only available (free and made to measure) to the labourers manhandling the heavy barrels of beer.

The quality of the paternalism that had existed in the company towards the 3000 or so employees suddenly began to come to me. To say that it was cradle to the grave comes close to the truth: non-contributory pensions; most employees given heavily subsidised housing, the blocks of Victorian terraces in Burton matched only by Coronation Street; the legendary annual outings to the seaside. During the years of the Depression in the 1930s not a single employee was laid off, leading to a heritage of families working for the company generation after generation. Even in death, evidence was turned up some years ago of coffin manufacture in the joiner's shop, with different metal fittings for the appropriate status (or rather ex-status) of the employee; iron for the workers, brass for the staff, silver for the directors. A company bier is well preserved in the great (now renamed) Bass Museum of Brewing History in Burton.

Finally, came a call to see the company secretary (not the personnel department, which did not seem to exist) and 'clock in' as an employee before starting in the brewery. This meant attendance at the company headquarters, with its own rules of behaviour that one had to learn pretty quickly.

On entry, one was faced by a magnificent double staircase, to be directed to left or right by a flunkey, and up which it was forbidden to proceed at anything but a sedate pace no matter how urgent the mission, paying due homage *en passant* to the Book of Remembrance set in the wall. Education in this protocol was closely monitored by the directors' senior secretary, seemingly invariably leaning over the top banister, whilst guarding the corridors of power from the *hoi polloi*. At a distance she resembled a mixture of queen bee and dragon, and sounded like one as I innocently took the stairs two at a time; but close to, her dowdy tweed skirt and incongruous men's tartan carpet slippers clearly told another story altogether. A matter for further research into the mysteries of senior management, I thought, as she accepted my presence on her territory without further comment.

Note to file: A sharp tongue or hard outer crust, on someone who is in a position of power, is nothing to fear. They all have a soft heart underneath; the key is to know how to get to it. Rather like a cactus or a pineapple, I suppose.

Proceeding along a corridor, peeping through an open office door, I was struck by a row of immaculately tidy young men sitting on stools at high Victorian desks, industriously working away at huge leather-bound ledgers. Never before had I seen such a Dickensian scene, as the supervisor strode around the room, hands behind his back, peering over the shoulders of the unfortunates. In fact, I soon learned that to work in the offices of the company was not unfortunate at all, but the prime ambition of many a local school leaver, carrying enormous kudos among one's peers. The only entry requirements were undemanding - tidiness, good manners, numeracy, neat writing and respect for one's elders. No wonder someone had to invent computers as these qualities vanished from the school outputs, or was it the latter that caused the former?

Safely recorded as an employee, I set off for the New Brewery, built in 1863.

A splendid brewer colleague - I shall call him Tom - introduced me to many of the ways of the time warp, having worked his way up from the bottom for seven years or so. His father-in-law was the group captain who had risked his Air Force career by being Winston Churchill's confidant of the true pitiful state of aircraft rearmament during the 1930s, whilst the government was reassuring the populace that everything was in hand to cope with the potential Nazi threat to the nation. As a boy, he had been semi-adopted by a member of the beerage, and well educated through brewing industry endowments; so when the time came to exit from the Air Force, it was almost natural that he should repay the patronage by applying his skills as a brewer. Thus totally unexpected relationships led to high quality family commitment to the company.

Not that such experiences were greatly welcomed by the traditional Burton head brewers. In fact, the Group Captain's greatest idea was that the end of the war would produce thousands of tons of scrap aluminium in the form of redundant aeroplanes, and that this metal would be ideal for making beer barrels to replace the heavy wooden variety. He arranged for all the directors of Short Brothers to visit the brewery and discuss the idea, only to be turned down flat by his own brewery directors. Twenty years later, the whole industry was awash with aluminium beer barrels.

Note to file: There really is nothing new under the sun, absolutely nothing if you go back far enough. It is just bad luck if you happen to have been born in the wrong time warp.

During the early 1960s Tom clearly benefited from this background, and was able to advance against a wide variety of odds. He had rapidly learnt that any suggestion to the head brewer of improving the process, or even sometimes just the asking of an intelligent technical question, would be treated as gross insubordination. How the young brewer of those days ever learnt his profession against such defensive measures of the powerful traditionalists remains a mystery; he was effectively powerless, but at least eternally grateful for his pitiful salary, which a few years before would have been *payment* to the head brewer for the privilege of an apprenticeship.

Management skills, on the other hand, were a lot easier to pick up through the daily routines of the shift brewer. The shift system was little different from any other industry working 24 hours a day, five or six days per week; each brewer would alternate on the morning, afternoon and night shifts weekly, followed by a week on 'days'. On shift, he would be effectively the sole manager of the routine brewing operation: when on 'days', he would be at the beck and call of the senior brewers, to experience all manner of (usually) unpleasant character-building tasks.

His reward was to be referred to as 'gentleman brewer' of the week, whilst the head brewer ensured that he carried out these tasks in a manner appropriate to that title. This included taking him on tow on the daily tour and inspection of the brewing operations. It was on these tours that the head brewer passed on his pearls of wisdom to the attentive but nervous youngsters, who had the eternal problem of having to conceal any thoughts or suggestions that might challenge the quality of the wisdom forthcoming.

It was Tom who had experienced an inspection of a beer vessel that had no 'head' of yeast on the surface, and was clearly not fermenting. The head brewer had peered into the flat dark surface, muttered a few words, and then told Tom that all would be well by the morrow. As early as possible, out of Tom's hearing, he told the supervisor to discipline the operator who had forgotten to put the yeast in, and to get it stirred in immediately so that on the next day the beer would be well away with its fermentation. On the next day's tour, when Tom asked the head brewer exactly what he had done to correct the fermentation, he replied "My boy, you will learn one day from experience *how* to look closely at a problem, analyse it and resolve it. And that is why *I* am the head brewer. And just in case, I also slipped three aspirins into the beer - that's always good for a bad head."

Note to file: Don't believe everything that your boss tells you. He often has other agendas to take into account at the same time, most probably of a self-preservation nature. Are all bosses like this?

In those glorious days of freedom from personnel departments, it often fell to the lot of the gentleman brewer to recruit people into any vacancies in the brewery workforce. This consisted of manning a small window in the outside wall of the brewer's office, to which anyone could present themselves as job applicants. Selection was based on smartness of appearance and personality. These were somewhat inappropriate to the task invariably given to new recruits, but nevertheless a cunning device to test the presence of character likely to be worthy of promotion later to a responsible job.

One lunchtime session all alone at the window, Tom had selected a particularly worthy-looking well-spoken individual, who was all too happy to report to the foreman of the hop press gang at 10 pm on the Sunday night, to spend his first night shift shovelling hot, wet, smelly used hops into railway wagons.

It so happened that Tom had moved from gentleman to night shift brewer that weekend, so was manager of that shift. Preparing himself to go home at 6am. on the Monday morning, the brewery yard suddenly filled with screaming police cars. Armed officers jumped out, surrounding the yard and yelling to everyone to take cover as they pinned Tom's new recruit to the wall, handcuffed him and bundled him into the back of one of the cars.

Tom, of course, was all too able to assist the police on the reason for the existence of the man on the site, adding meaningful thoughts about his suspicious appearance and behaviour, the need for keeping a wary eye on him, and the convenience of the brewery yard as a trap. So Tom gained considerable kudos for his contribution to the recapture of an infamous serial killer on the run from Leicester jail.

Note to file: To advance yourself in the eyes of your employer, being in the right place at the right time, and the ability to cover a hole that you dug yourself, are probably more important than any other strategy.

Tom, in fact, became quite a dab hand at proving the truth of that note. Again as gentleman brewer, it was part of the job in busy brewing weeks to come in and start the first brew of the week on Sunday at 2pm and remain in charge of the brewery until 6pm when the normal full shift came on. In fact, there was nothing else to do after putting in the first brew, which took only 20 minutes, which coincided conveniently with the start of the Sunday cinema programme just round the corner from the brewery. Thus it became an unwritten, totally unauthorized practice that the brewer could be recalled from the cinema if urgently required.

On the occasion in question, at the climax of the critical love scene, a message was flashed on the screen requesting the brewer to return to the brewery, as it was on fire. To howls of delight from the audience, Tom dashed off, to find the brewery's own fire brigade in full control of extinguishing a disappointingly minor conflagration, just as the town's fire engine appeared around the corner.

First thing on Monday morning, the head brewer arrived looking unusually excitable, looked around the office and asked sternly "Who is gentleman this week?" Tom could not avoid admitting this dubious privilege, desperately trying to control his shaky knees.

"Well done, my boy," he announced loudly, for all and sundry to take note. "Smart bit of action yesterday afternoon. Saved a lot of problems, and no doubt a few lives as well. You can take the day off."

"Thank you very much," replied Tom calmly, as if he was worthy of at least a raise as well, adding honestly and truthfully "I wish that I could have done more."

Note to file: An ounce of image may be worth a pound of performance, but don't press your luck *too* far.

Disciplinary matters in the mid 1960s were always difficult, in the absence of any personnel policy, and with a workforce enjoying the benefits of a thoroughly paternalistic approach to employment for a large number of families over several generations. But there are limits, beyond which one has to take appropriate measures to maintain the credibility of management and good order.

One day gentleman Tom was summoned by the head brewer and told to do something useful for a change, by sacking an operator known for years as 'Moaner' Bates, because he (the head brewer) had taken enough of his continual complaining. Tom dutifully reported back his mission as fully accomplished, whereupon the head brewer pulled out Bates' personal file from the roll-top Victorian desk and entered 'dismissed for impertinence to my brewers'. The following day, Tom discovered 'Moaner' Bates working as normal.

"I sacked you yesterday, Bates," cried Tom, furious at the ridiculous scenario, and the snub to his authority.

"I know," replied Bates, "but I also knew that you didn't mean it."

It was time to elegate (delegate upwards) the problem back to the head brewer, thought Tom, certain that he would want to be the one to deal with such insubordination to one of his brewers. But Tom's luck was not there that day; the head brewer simply told *him* to do something about Bates complaining all the time.

*

Note to file: There are always limits to which you can be expected to tolerate. But don't expect your boss to take any notice of them.

My first week of training in the brewery was in gentleman mode, except that this descriptive word had been recently erased from the brewery language, in deference to the style of the new head brewer. Here was the work and the genius of Sir at his very best. The first of the last old traditional head brewers had retired (only two left in the other two breweries), and Sir had decided to replace him with the complete antithesis of all that two centuries of paternal dictatorship had set in concrete. This excluded, of course, the required passion for the unique quality of the beers emanating from the mecca of brewing.

I shall refer to this new phenomenon as Arthur, larger than life in all senses of the word. As a schoolboy he was so enthusiastic about rugby that after his first few games he is reputed to have written home '...I have decided that when I grow up I am going to play rugger for England. I have already broken an arm. Fortunately it wasn't mine...' When he was told that he would not make the school rugby team unless he was at least 14 stone, he accepted this challenge with typical cheerful dynamism; judging by his stature and demeanour ten years later, he must have succeeded with plenty to spare.

The 1960s was the peak of the era when it was easy to become a legend in one's own lunchtime. Time meant nothing to Arthur; all human contact at work was geared to sheer enthusiasm and dedication to the excellence of his beer, whilst all human contact socially was geared to...well...sheer enthusiasm and dedication to the excellence of his beer. Consumption levels and accompanying blotting paper (food) created such an indistinguishable division between his work and his leisure that it became extremely easy to deal with him.

We assumed, correctly, 24-hour availability.

His reputation was admired by several of the company's other senior brewers, whose own timeless egos and reputations were largely based on the possession of hollow legs. But crisis came when one of them, a certain Ken, was sent to America with Arthur for two weeks to investigate some brewing technique or another; here was a major challenge to the older guard, facing the threat of a new-age young parvenu, with no way out from public humiliation if Arthur was to drink and eat him under the table. On return from the trip, Ken was seen with his face wreathed in smiles, telling everyone that Arthur had been as sick as a dog during the whole fortnight, and had never managed more than a 26 oz steak at any meal.

Note to file: When you know that you are not in the same league, it is better to admit it rather than trust to luck that you will not be found out.

Not that Arthur would have deliberately humiliated anyone, he was far too nice a guy for that; he wanted everyone to have the same level of extrovert *joie de vivre* that he himself possessed. His enthusiasm overflowed into a puzzled type of respect from his brewing staff, when his promotion above them had followed two recent classic cardinal sins that a brewer should, at best, only survive (as opposed to getting promotion). The first was to ignore a temporary company moratorium on capital expenditure; his project at the time was far too important to be held up by such minor irritations that could not possibly apply to him, and he had placed a huge unauthorized order for capital equipment.

The second was more obvious to all and sundry, when Arthur caused the collapse of a large beer tank. The sight of a tangled mass of crumpled metal sheets, during the months necessary to replace them, should have been as bad a penalty in shame and embarrassment as the normal dressing down for such carelessness. But such was the esteem for Arthur's handling of these crises that when, ten years later, I was in charge of the brewery and a tank mysteriously collapsed for no obvious reason, I received a queue of brewers willing to accept responsibility. Such was the unwritten folklore established by Arthur.

Note to file: Some people can get away with anything. Be envious, rather than try to imitate it yourself.

The 1960s were seeing the beginning of staff rewards and incentives other than salary, and to the eternal credit of Sir, who had noted company cars creeping into the marketing end of the business, decided that his brewers were just as important, and anyway they needed to get round the pubs as much if not more than anyone else. The first tentative step was that the new head brewer should have a company car appropriate to his status and personal choice, this being a Ford Zodiac. I was in Arthur's office when Alec-the-car-administrator phoned him to confirm the allocation of the car, and what colour would he like?

"Any colour of green will do, Alec, so long as you can get it to me tomorrow", beamed Arthur down the phone.

"The only one available at the dealers for immediate delivery is aubergine", Alec told him.

"That's a nice colour of green, I'll take it", said Arthur's mouth, as the rest of him swelled with excitement, putting down the phone before I could suggest a moment for a little rethink. Not that Arthur ever had time for such backward reflection, when his unique talent of being able to get on his horse and ride off in all directions was in full swing.

The following morning his purple monstrosity arrived in the brewery yard; Arthur clearly fell in love with it instantly, and spent the rest of the morning drooling over it and reading the instruction manual. One thing to be said about Arthur is that he was not a man of 'if all else fails, read the instructions'; far from it, his inclinations tended towards noting carefully everything that the maker had to say, but then being somewhat selective about what he thought was worthy of his retention.

Arthur could not wait to go home for lunch and show off his shiny new toy to his wife, and to use the A38 to try it out. The mid-1960s were the days before the A38 became a permanent warehouse for surplus traffic cones. On returning to the office he immediately rang Alec to complain that the car would not do the quoted maximum speed of 115 mph.

"But Arthur," pleaded Alec, "you've got a brand new machine there."

"Precisely," Arthur replied, "if it won't do it now, when will it?"

Note to file: Beware of large jolly drivers in large purple cars.

Continuing my week's instruction for shift brewing, I learnt the details of the daily beer allowance, which seemed to consist of everyone receiving a strictly defined ration, depending on the hours worked and the actual job, the ration being calculated on both volume and strength of the beer, issued and monitored by the shift brewer.

Thank goodness for the slide rule, I thought, as I was told of the frothing jugs of best bitter to be delivered to the various 'cabins' (rest rooms) and the watered down T-beer for the 'grainers' and the further watered down Lack beer for the 'slackies'. But surely, I thought, there must be enough authorized beer floating about to satisfy everyone's needs without having to *control* it, let alone having to find out who or what grainers and slackies were.

At least I had an explanation for one strange daily phenomenon, when one of the men going home clearly had great difficulty in co-ordinating his feet with the pedals of his bicycle. At first I had thought that he had some awkward unfortunate disability, until I discovered that he was the keeper of the allowance beer cellar.

I also learnt how to deal with the wages, being slightly

alarmed at the security measures when wage packets were left loose on the brewers' office table - 'Oh, Joe's off sick, his neighbour Jack on the night shift will pick it up for him when he goes home tomorrow morning' was a typical instruction, in this case adding "Jack's the mash room foreman - he cuts the head brewer's hair, professional hairdresser he was, he'd probably do yours between mashes if you ask him nicely." That's funny, I thought, the head brewer's bald.

I toured the brewery with a brewer and learnt the rudiments of what a shift brewer has to do, which is to 'mash in' and control the excise duty 'collection', and to be a wise, knowledgeable checker, counsellor and decision-taker of every other operation that the men had been doing routinely for decades.

Lots of samples seemed to be taken which then disappeared, presumably to the laboratory, because I never saw a lab technician in the brewery. Except once, when a whole army of them descended on one of the dozens of Burton union sets (the fermentation system unique to Burton) for the annual swabbing check for cleanliness. I discovered subsequently that it was named the Lab union set, and was never used for making beer.

Someone mysteriously warned me to avoid night shifts when there is a full moon, but without any mention of why or how.

I was quickly identified by the operators as being 'different' from the other young shift brewers fresh out from university, being a good ten years older than them. It was an opportunity for the operators to use me as some sort of wise owl, in the apparent absence of an identifiable personnel department, or indeed organized trade union:

"Why do I have to take orders from £1000-a-year young whippersnapper shift brewers with no experience?" an aggrieved operator asked me.

"How much do you take home?" I asked back.

"I only get £29 a week," he moaned.

Note to file: There's more to managing people than meets the eye. Or, for that matter, any other part of the anatomy that might get in the way of irate workers.

CHAPTER 3

LEARNING THE HARD WAY

Shift working is just another work routine that most people can fairly easily get used to. It has its advantages and disadvantages; one's social life relative to the masses is necessarily of a different order, but there are many things that you can do better during a weekday when the masses are conveniently out of the way at work. I discovered that many of the permanent shift workers were ace golfers, to the fury of their golfing managers who could only play at the weekend. To try to correct the balance in this town of one golf club, a representative group of managers from the company's HQ ivory tower had organized a deputation to the club to ask it to deny shift-working members access to the course at weekends.

Note to file: The battle for human rights among the downtrodden workers clearly needs to go far beyond getting attitudes right in their workplace alone.

One advantage of working shifts is the rapport that one experiences among the whole shift team in the absence of direct senior managerial control, invoking a sense of joint responsibility to get the whole job done well. This will include covering each other's jobs in the event of temporary absence or indisposition, physical or mental, and can extend even to permanent coverage of a weakness in a 'good mate' who is truthfully unfit for work.

This was all splendidly illustrated on my first week of night shifts. Coming in on the Wednesday night at 10 pm., there was a message for me in the shift brewer's in-tray, composed in a style and logic capable only of coming from Arthur, instructing me to sack the mash-room foreman the following Friday night for being drunk.

Note to file: There is nothing like effective advanced planning.

Come the Friday night, it was clear from the start that things were not going to go precisely as planned. The supervisor, a splendid man of presence and command named Jack Hegg, had failed to turn up, as had the nicest of quiet men, Sam Bacon the 'sugar' man. Worse, having had a week of cloudy skies, the sky had suddenly cleared to reveal the biggest, brightest full moon that I had seen.

A mixture of apprehension and anticipation overwhelmed me as we set about the brewing, distinctly short on both experienced supervision and a full complement of men, and a horrendous expectation that all would be revealed concerning the warning I had been given about full moons.

Fortunately, the two absentees turned up at midnight, very shamefaced. They had both been arrested by a policeman when cycling together across the Trent footbridge on the way to the brewery. On demanding their names to put into his police notebook, Sam obligingly gave his name as Bacon. "Oh yes," said the copper, turning to Jack, "and I suppose your name is Egg?"

"Yes," Jack Hegg replied.

"Right then," snapped the law, "it's down to the station the pair of you. I'm not having you make a right fool of me."

Come 2 am., things seemed to be moving a bit more towards target. Much of the shift's beer allowance seemed to have found its way to the mash room 'cabin', and the foreman was showing suitable signs of inebriation. This confirmed my view that there was enough beer allowance sloshing around the brewery to accommodate more than anyone's needs, however demanding they might be. Returning to the brewer's office, I passed the sugar room to see, not Sam, but a mate of his doing his work. When I asked him the whereabouts of Sam, I received a non-committal grunt and a hand signal of indeterminate clarity. Shrugging my shoulders, I left and proceeded across the brewery yard to espy, on an open footbridge across the yard, the figure of Sam oscillating from side to side, completely away with the fairies as he sung his incomprehensible mumbling to the huge shining orb in the sky. I crept discreetly into the office.

Note to file: Discretion is the better part of quite a lot of other important things. It seems to be quite a useful management tool.

By 4 am. the mash room foreman was also well away, enough for me to go to his assistant to tell him to finish off the brew, as clearly his senior was practically incapable.

"I can't," he said, "I'm only under training."

Unwilling to admit to him that I was in exactly the same boat, and bearing in mind that this was the end of the last brew of the week, I judged that the minimum collateral damage would be done by letting the inebriated foreman complete the task before sacking him; useful discretion again. Thus it was at 5am. that I dismissed him.

He was just able to take this in, and to indicate that no way was he going to accept the sack from me, and that he wished to speak to his best friend Arthur. Aware of previous abortive attempts by young brewers to sack men on instructions from the head brewer, and although it was 5 am. on a Saturday morning, I judged it apt to get Arthur involved, and anyway it would serve him right for landing me in this hole. I rang the security officer to attend the brewer's office (discretion again) either as witness, or for eviction, or any other unforeseen requirement for assistance, and took the foreman down to the external phone in the office.

My phone call rang for several minutes before Arthur's sleepy wife answered.

"Sorry, Beryl," I said, "I know it's 5 o'clock, but I must speak to Arthur."

"He's been out in the trade trying out the new beer. I'll go and see if he's back yet," she replied.

Note to file: There is no limit to the degree of commitment that you can give in support of the products for which you are responsible.

A feature of all large breweries was the omnipresence of HM Customs & Excise, and the proportion of time spent by brewers in satisfying their requirements. Back in 1966, breweries were heaving with excise officers. Bass had at least twelve in Burton-on-Trent alone, most of whom were 'resident', meaning employed full time on the one company site.

The main reason for this was, of course, the ludicrous system for raising the excise duty before the beer was even fermented, requiring a vast administration system of double and triple checks that all the beer eventually leaving the brewery, generally between two and six weeks later, was accounted for as having been charged for duty. The system had been invented in 1880 as the simplest method of measuring volume and strength in a largely rural unscientific industry - a dipstick into a gauged vessel, and a floating saccharometer to measure original gravity - and remained unaltered for 113 years despite the wonders of 20th century technology.

The power of the Excise in a brewery was infinite, still ever suspicious and living on a single fraud some 35 years before, of a brewery being caught brewing on a Sunday without entry into the excise book, and bypassing the gauged vessels used for collecting the duty. However, by the mid 1960s, most privately-owned breweries had already been sold to large public companies, and anyway the incentive to cheat the Excise was of a much lower order, if not non-existent.

Note to file: Autonomous revenue-raising bodies answerable to no-one are like elephants. Not only do they have long memories, you have to do everything to avoid them either treading on you, or charging at you, or heavily defecating upon you from a great height.

Inevitably, working relationships had to be established with the 'resident' excise officers. They had their obligatory checking duties laid down, whilst the brewers were constrained by almost impossible demands to enter accurately in the excise book, in advance, every detail of every action relating to the use of or movement of any material that might conceivably give rise to a check by the excise officer that it tallied with the duty charge; and to enter the time of intention to do it, and to enter the completion of that action within a certain time limit.

It is small wonder that the brewers had little time to think about the future. When there was a technical advance it required negotiation with the Excise for an 'indulgence' away from the set routines, but with no relief from the archaic rules of 1880 if the indulgence was subsequently found to be detrimental to the duty payable.

My increasing personal belief, I suppose natural to a trained scientist, had to be that we were dealing here with perfectly straightforward highly organised insanity, ingrained since 1880. This was later irrecoverably confirmed, in my mind, when I learnt about the promiscuous surveys of the brewery that each excise officer had to undertake, by law, at irregular intervals. Not being aware of the existence of any appropriate facilities or other relevant resources likely to promote promiscuity around the brewery, I decided to let this wash over me rather than investigate further, in the hope that I would not have the misfortune to be on duty when one of these occurred.

Lexicographers, who are better at the English language than I, may well scoff at my ignorance. In fact, reference to a good dictionary will not only reveal the simple answer, but also confirm the archaic nature of the beast we were dealing with; whoever would have thought that 'promiscuous' could mean something entirely different in the dim and distant past?

Note to file: There is always an identifiable system in any madness.

Mad the system may have been, but at least it got the results that the Chancellor of the Exchequer wanted, whilst surprisingly providing ample opportunity for brewers and resident excise men to develop personal as well as working relationships, albeit verging on the eccentric from time to time. It was probably this mutual eccentricity that kept everybody (or nearly everybody) sane, whilst working such a strict regime, under the permanent stifling mistrust emanating from the local excise headquarters.

Theoretically, all that the brewery companies were required to do was to provide conveniently placed rooms for excise use, equipped with a chair, and a table on which to keep the excise book. In practice, it required all manner of conveniences for verbal communication and adaptation of the pettiest of the complex rules, to keep sizeable, fast brewing operations running smoothly. Not that every officer was inclined to, or even capable of such adaptation; certainly there was no obligation on them.

Fortunately, such animals were rare, and did not seem to last very long; the reason for this may be that doing everything mindlessly by the book was one of the routes to fast track promotion in that part of the Civil Service.

A particularly obnoxious officer, fresh to the brewing industry, demanded a certain size and quality of desk and carpet appropriate to his job grade, as laid down in some Civil Service manual of employment conditions. This was my first lesson in getting the most out of a difficult relationship situation.

Note to file: Never give a direct 'no' to an unreasonable request, particularly when you need to develop the enquirer's co-operation. To keep them hanging on in hope, have a battery of responses appropriate to the occasion, which might range from 'definitely maybe' to 'I'll put it in year 4 of my 3-year plan'.

Our days were lightened by the influence of one of the senior officers who, when requested by us to allow, for instance, a certain operation to take place at a different time than that specified in the rules, would invariably take a moment's thought, and then pronounce:

'In my opinion, if I allow this, Her Majesty will still be able to sleep soundly tonight, in the full confidence that her revenues are safe and secure, so go ahead and do it!'

Through this kind of relationship many officers identified themselves with the life and objectives of the business, which inevitably led to them to being accepted in many ways almost as members of staff. They certainly qualified for beer allowance (duty paid, of course), premium car parking, and access to the communication hub of the brewery (the sample store). These and other human niceties certainly made their work more fulfilling, and led sometimes to lasting domestic friendships with brewing staff.

The associated sympathy we had towards our old resident excise officers caused much reminiscing of old times. It turned out that, according to one of them with a historical bent, our brewery was possibly the only one that had ever been able to get an excise officer sacked; officially, of course, their behaviour had nothing to do with the brewery.

A particularly miserable officer had decided to undertake a sideline from his routine job, and had taken up breeding a few pigs. Unfortunately, he was accustomed to coming into the brewery with his Wellington boots fresh from the sty. Continual complaints from the head brewer to the local surveyor of excise eventually caused the man to be threatened with disciplinary action if he persisted with this anti-social activity.

The officer took no notice of the instruction, was eventually summoned to the surveyor and ordered to hand in his resignation. This required him to write a letter, in the then standard Civil Service format, commencing *'Honourable Sirs, I have the honour to submit my resignation ....'* There and then he wrote his letter and handed it to the surveyor. He took one look at it, blanched, handed it back and ordered him to amend the opening, if only because of the sensitivity of the female administrators at headquarters who would deal with the letter. He had, in fact, started his letter *'Honourable Buggers, I have the honour ....'* Thinking for a few moments, he brought out his pen, crossed out *'Honourable'*, handed the letter back and calmly walked out.

*

Note to file: There is more than one way of getting satisfaction from becoming involved with pigs.

Retracing steps to 1966, life in the brewery was dominated by Arthur, unconsciously treating the spread of his enthusiasm as a team building exercise. This terminology, of course, did not exist at that date, any more than Outward Bound's dozens of homologues did, spun off from management theories yet to be invented, and the accompanying fortunes to be made by people who would never have been anywhere near managing a workforce.

Arthur's weekends would consist of hill walking trips in Wales for the brewers, with the express intention on each return journey to find a different pub, where they could drink it dry of Worthington White Shield, Arthur's favourite tipple.

On one occasion they found a tiny hostelry in the middle of nowhere, the shelves of which were packed solid with nothing but bottles of this favoured beverage. Observing that this was going to be quite a challenge for his five thirsty brewers, Arthur called for the landlord, announced that he was the head brewer of the beer, and required instant service for his thirsting brewers.

Far from being impressed, the landlord refused to serve him, explaining that all the beer was reserved for one customer, and he could only get deliveries once a week.

"Wonderful," enthused Arthur, "I'll invite you both to the brewery for a fabulous day out, and get you and your pub the best publicity you've ever had."

*

Note to file: Always put your customers first even if you, yourself, have to go without.

It was around this time that a certain degree of caution was beginning to be required in the matter of drinking and driving. Testing of urine samples was coming into vogue in preference to testing the ability to walk in a straight line. One of our brewers, pseudonym Hugo, was a rich young man with no living family ties, whose favourite pastime was driving the most powerful sports cars that money could buy.

He temporarily solved this worrying threat to his life style by devising a concealed apparatus in his underwear, whereby he was capable of delivering, even under supervision, an alcohol-free urine sample. On the one and only occasion that he used it, he subsequently realised the mistake of not submitting a sample with *some* alcohol in it; so, instead of being able to crow about his ability to fox the police, they never ceased hounding him for fooling them.

Hugo was not the most successful brewer of all time. As a graduate he could hardly have been short of grey matter; it was more the speed of his intellectual processes that created minor difficulties, which manifested themselves in the form of moments of apparent poor connection between eye and brain. This, of course, could not be observed over the telephone at the time that he was responsible for organizing the next week's brewing, and had forgotten to order the malt; the head maltster sarcastically enquired whether he was going to brew any beer the next week, to which Hugo replied that he was not sure, but he would find out and ring back.

Note to file: Always keep your options open on your work plans. But not too obviously. Meanwhile, try not to behave routinely as if the day has started without you.

When he had his inevitable car crash, it was concerning that he had effectively disappeared, being untraceable for lack of next of kin. After four days, Sir received a phone call from a distant hospital. After general relief at both ends of the line, the doctor expressed his extreme concern about Hugo's condition; he had been in a coma for three days, but now that he had come round, there was grave concern about his ability to respond fast enough to external stimuli, and his eyes were continually showing a glazed expression.

"Great!" cried Sir down the phone, "That's totally normal. I'll send someone round tomorrow to bring him back."

Arthur decided to take the drink-drive scenario a lot more responsibly than initially Hugo had. It was up to the brewers to lead the way in sensible acknowledgement of the rules as the government developed the law. The first action he took was to arrange that, on all expeditions around the pubs to check the beer quality, chauffeurs would be used. The first time we went out, he asked the chauffeurs to come into each pub and have a drink on him, and took grave offence when they refused.

In his efforts to gain support from his brewers at the level of his own enthusiasm and bonhomie, Arthur's expeditions always contained some new team-building experience, forgetting that others might have homes to go to occasionally, where their wives might have a stronger say on whether their loved ones were in or not at 5 am.

Fortunately, these events declined rapidly in popularity after Arthur took some of his team into a Turkish bath, in which Arthur had an unfortunate experience with a loofah in the hands of a huge muscle-bound attendant, who, Arthur claimed, had taken an unsolicited fancy to him.

His attention then turned to the 'Oktoberfest' beer festival held annually in Munich. This is the only October beer festival where most of it is held in September, presumably because the enthusiastic Bavarians cannot wait for any chance to celebrate their natural heritage. What better place for Arthur to express his personality and leadership than in huge beer halls, consuming endless steins of foaming German beer and whole spit-roasted chickens, singing and dancing (on the tables) to the top German Oompah bands?

Ever keen to learn new things about this wonderful brewing world, he was particularly impressed by the sensitivity of German officialdom in dealing with those celebrants who could not quite make it to the exit at closing time each night. A thorough search of the site is made, all comatose bodies are carefully carried to a warm place for recuperation, and suitable nourishment (medical or otherwise) provided the following morning, before allowing them back into the real world. How Arthur loved all this.

This annual event certainly caught the imagination of the brewers, because attendance was regular, using their own holiday allowance and at their own expense. But it was only once a year; so, bitten by the international bug, Arthur deemed it necessary that his brewers should start becoming adept at foreign languages, and enrolled them on a French course at a local college.

One of them, in fact, found a talent he did not know he had and became extremely proficient in business French, to the point of wishing to develop his career on the international scene. However, although we had an international operation, which included beers uniquely brewed for distribution and expansion throughout francophone countries, not a bleep of interest was shown in using this man's new-found skills. The boss of that operation did have a double-barrelled name, components of which had beerage connections, thus raising anyway the question of the long-term nature of anyone's role in that outfit.

*

Note to file: By all means develop your wider talents yourself, but don't expect your existing employer to take any notice of them particularly if your latest acquired skill would outclass your boss.

One of the highlights of shift work was the opportunity, when on the 'gentleman' shift of 9-to-5 day work, to enjoy one's beer allowance in the sample store, in the company of all the brewers, plus Allied Trader visitors selling their wares and preparing to take brewers out to lunch, and sundry local businessmen who made up the head brewer's 'court'. This was indeed the true hub of any brewery in those days, but the scale of the Bass operation was of outstanding proportions, reflecting the huge volumes of beer production and its widespread distribution across the whole country.

The most important function of a sample store, of course, was to keep one cask of every individual batch, perhaps six per day on average, under perfect storage conditions for the expected maximum life in the trade of six weeks. This was by far the best quality check on the durability of the cask-conditioned beers, and a reference point in the event of any trade comment on any particular brew. Thus did visitors enjoy the company's hospitality in a vast, impressive 100-year-old cellar, surrounded by the best part of 200 casks perfectly arrayed and carefully tended.

The subsidiary function of the sample store was as a communication forum where, under the agreeable social ambiance of beer flowing, always in perfect condition, it was difficult to miss anything of significance going on in any of the breweries in the country, as the Allied Traders tried to extend their sales of new products and processes.

On top of all this, the sample store had an 'inner sanctum', within which the head brewer entertained special friends and customers, thus creating not only a hierarchy of importance among regular visitors, but also intense rivalry and ambition amongst them to gain access to this (remarkably uncomfortable) facility. This was right up Arthur's street, as a means of expressing and developing his impressively extrovert style and he included the inner sanctum as a means of disposal of a measurable proportion of the company's production of his favourite bottled Worthington White Shield down the throats of his favoured few.

Beyond the inner sanctum lay, literally, the store of all the 'laying down' beers that had been brewed over the previous 100 years, starting with a beer of 1869 brewed for the 21st birthday of a director's son. In 1969, the last remaining member of the family in Burton was entertained to a centenary celebration lunch, at which the beer was sampled and judged to be in excellent form. No-one outside the company experienced the store and its contents, which included the world famous King's Ale of 1902. Neither was the size of the stocks revealed, except that it was sufficient to release, traditionally, the 'last one' of any of the brews for the occasional charitable cause.

In the interests of economy, the running of the sample store was always in the hands of only one employee; this was invariably a man of enormous integrity, experienced in beer handling, and of such a pleasant and confident disposition that it allowed him to treat the most important visitors as equals in conversation, whilst showing appropriate respect for their social and company standing.

It was surprising how many of such candidates, always taken from the 'shop floor', filled these positions over the years, and became well known throughout the brewing fraternity as perfectly reflecting the status, standing and style of the company.

Note to file: If you need a modern-day Jeeves to complete your front line company presence, they are not as difficult to find as you might think. Look further down the hierarchy.

*

In my three months of shift working, it was of great interest to observe attitudes in the brewery towards quality control. After all, this was what I was going to be involved most in, working from the laboratory, and my previous experiences had identified a clear resistance of brewers in general to delegate beer quality to those who knew more than them about it.

As described in a previous chapter, there was always considerable freedom to decide how sterile the brewing operation needed to be, whilst still conforming to food standards. Since over 90 per cent of beer consumed at that time came anyway from an open cask in a pub cellar, with no direct control over its handling there, one could well question the necessity for the tightest quality standards when the beer left the brewery.

One was aware of many samples being taken by the brewery operators, which were then sent to the laboratory during the course of the day. Most of the analytical results seemed to be posted back to the head brewer's office in irregular batches; nothing seemed to come of them in terms of any control adjustments to the brewing process, which appeared to have been laid down in concrete by the brewers alone.

One exception to the delays in reporting scientific analyses was a vital sample taken from every wort, with the results being delivered back by hand the next day. This was the analysis of 'angle' for each wort, and was so important that it had to be entered in the brewing book in red ink ('scratcher' pen, red ink and blotter provided). As I recall, the desired figure was 147 degrees, and which varied, from time to time, a few degrees either way. No one ever queried or discussed these figures that stood out in red from the pages of the leather-bound brewing book, and anyway they still came too late to do anything about them, the wort having long started to turn itself into beer.

I opted for the likelihood that the analysis was invented in the distant past, and then maintained by tradition, to the point where no-one knew or remembered what the figures really signified. As a matter of discretion, I decided, as a scientist, not to give any impression of ignorance of the subject, and to set myself the target of finding out the truth at a more suitable time.

Note to file: Be sympathetic towards highly disciplined but outdated management controls; it is the fact that a strong discipline exists which is the most important. The controls can then be worked on at an appropriate time and speed.

I was ready for the lab.

CHAPTER 4

USING SUPPORT FACILITIES

In the 1960s, the laboratory was situated in a convenient corner of the enormous brewery site. I say convenient, in the sense that it was out of the way of anyone who wished to brew their beer without having to think about any scientific involvement; and at the same time the senior lab staff could carry out uninterrupted research work, which they knew would be beneficial to those who *did* value scientific back-up to their jobs.

Thus existed a quasi-autonomous scientific establishment reporting to Sir, and Sir alone, who was steadily building up the strength, status and influence of the lab in the daily running of the brewing process. To this end, the boss of the lab had been recruited from the top of one of the top university brewing schools, as a result of which young blood started to come in, to supplement the excellent but long-serving scientists trained in the ways of yesteryear.

Dr Cyril Rainbow had rapidly established himself as a fount of all scientific knowledge on brewing matters, and became in great demand to solve all manner of quality problems, for those brewers who were prepared to bury their pride by asking for his help. These requests became increasingly numerous as the size of the company increased, incorporating more modern breweries, employing brewers who had rather less obvious God-like aspirations.

Cyril scored particularly highly with colleagues through his quiet, cultured style; one rather priggish head brewer paid him the compliment that 'he has never solved any of my problems, but he has always given me the confidence to solve them myself!' Nothing could better express the perfect role of a service function in solving other people's practical problems.

*

Note to file: Effective contribution of a service function towards solving problems is entirely dependent on the respect that that function commands. This includes, most importantly, its ability to preserve the dignity of the user.

On arrival at the lab, I received a guided tour from a bright, keen young graduate called Ken, who was the first of the new-look approach to staffing the lab. The research section, which had been built as a condition that Cyril imposed in accepting his appointment, was well equipped with all the modern scientific gadgetry of the time, including a new fangled device called a deep freeze. The purpose of this mysterious white chest had attracted the chairman's attention while officially opening the department. Cyril had explained the advantages of keeping samples in suspended frozen animation, for future analysis, reference, and experimentation.

This concept was so new to the chairman that he asked to see inside this latest wonder of science. Cyril himself was also somewhat taken aback when he lifted the lid, to reveal the chest packed with salmon, trout and sundry produce from his staff's vegetable gardens. The chairman had been tickled pink, enquiring how he could get hold of one for his home.

Note to file: There is nothing like keeping up with technological advance, and exploring its domestic potential before it ever reaches the home.

Proceeding on the tour, Ken showed me the cellar, within which was centrally situated a beautifully-made mahogany box sitting on a table, surrounded by a wealth of electric motors, drive bands and gear wheels that Heath Robinson himself would have been proud of. Enquiring of the use put to this strange contraption, Ken told me of the time when exports of the finest bottled ales to America were only allowed by the directors to travel in the hold of the Queen Mary. These beers were of the type that continue to condition and mature in the bottle, and a quality problem at some time in the past had been attributed by the brewers to the adverse effect of the sea journey. There had, of course, been no suggestion that the lab should investigate whether, in fact, the beer had been fit to travel in the first place.

This wonderful machine, called 'Queen Mary', was constructed in the company's engineering workshops, to simulate the pitching and rolling of the ship on its five-day crossing of the Atlantic. This allowed sample bottles to be placed in the beautiful mahogany box for five days and, if successfully submitted to this regime, authority would be given by the head brewer for despatch to America.

I then met the highly qualified graduate who had spent his entire working life analyzing every batch of malt used in the brewery. It says a lot for loyalty in a paternalistic environment, when one can gain such satisfaction from a highly specialized routine, particularly when the use made of the analyses is necessarily of limited application; the beer had invariably been brewed before the analytical results were ever reported.

He happened also to be the chemist who had the apparatus to measure the 'angle' of the wort of each brew, which had caused me such embarrassment a few weeks before. He explained to me how this measurement was useful in times gone past for forecasting how well the fermentation of the wort into beer would proceed, but since the war the quality of the malt and control of the process made such analyses outdated. He was amazed to be told that these were still highlighted in red ink in the brewing ledgers, but when I asked him why he was still doing these analyses every day, he replied, "No one has ever asked me to stop".

Others in the lab had equally shown their loyalty to the company, in their own special way. One day, one of the scientists was walking across the brewery yard on the way to work in the lab, when he saw a road tanker start to draw away from a filling point with the filling hose still connected. When the hose tightened, then snapped the valve off the tanker in front of his very eyes, he instantly whipped off his jacket and stuffed enough of it into the discharging beer to stem the flow, thus saving the best part of 1000 gallons of beer. His loyalty was recognized by a special commendation from on high, but no mention of a new jacket.

The chief analyst, Frank, was a lay preacher, an Oxford graduate and a splendid disciplinarian in teaching young lab assistants all about hard work and accuracy at the lab bench. This was not always easy for the young men, who were diverted by equivalent numbers of young female lab assistants, not averse to demonstrating their physical features, particularly in the summer, underneath their somewhat flimsy white lab coats, to the acute embarrassment and displeasure of Frank.

He would try to counteract such behaviour by telling the young men that, if they were really interested, all they had to do was to go down to the ale bank and admire the women working there, humping the full hogsheads (54 gallons) into the railway wagons; there was an ample supply of 50-inchers there.

They were, of course, extremely amusing characters, and would have been delighted at the chance to introduce the young lads to a bit of life's experience. They were also ready to show their company loyalty, when required: when the hoist broke down that lifted the hogsheads about three feet onto the railway platform, the men went on strike when ordered to lift them by hand. The women saved the company's fortunes by doing it for them

Note to file: In many respects, it is *men* who have been struggling for equality since the dawn of time.

Frank also had his own loyalties. He had spent a long career being chief chemist of the Worthington brewery until it had been shut, when their beer brands were transferred with him to the Bass breweries. Bass and Worthington brands had been deliberately sold to the public as if from different companies since their merger in 1926, creating fierce loyalties for one or the other among the consumers of these nationally distributed beers.

Some of these would now start their life in the same fermenting vessels. Frank solved his loyalty problem. When such samples came in with a dual label, he would religiously divide the sample in two, analyzing separately for Worthington and Bass: invariably his pet Worthington sample would be reported as spot on specification, whilst the Bass analysis would be slightly adrift.

Note to file: Company loyalty has many facets, both beneficial and rather less so. In a paternalistic environment, one is rewarded by job satisfaction, security and the chance of at least slightly eccentric enjoyment. Adversely, be prepared for a certain meanness of spirit from above: this is not intentional, but as a result of little knowledge of how the other 99.9 per cent live. On balance, it's not a bad existence.

The first time that I met the chief microbiologist, I wondered how he managed to cope with his microscope. It wasn't my responsibility to comment on the quality of anyone's eyesight, but I noted mentally that if the lenses fell out of his spectacles, one would be able to play marbles with them. This characteristic, however, in no way inhibited him from exercising authoritative analysis of the microbiological state of the beer, which was much respected but, as previously indicated, rarely acted on by the brewers.

Young Ken told me of his unfortunate experience when the microbiologist was on holiday, and he had been delegated to do the regular Friday afternoon job of looking under the microscope at samples from all the bottles maturing in the acres of vaulted cellars beneath the town, and sending the routine report to the head brewer. This Ken did, entering opposite the long vertical list of brew numbers a complete breakdown of all the organisms present in each sample; even Ken thought that it looked a bit like a domestic woodworm survey of Latin names, enough to scare the pants off anyone.

All went well until after the microbiologist returned from his fortnight's holiday, when he received a roasting telephone call from the head brewer, demanding to know why the beers had suddenly changed their microbiological condition so dramatically. Forget that it had taken him two weeks to notice, and that if there had been a real change, the inference was that it was nothing to do with the man who actually brewed the beer.

Ken, of course, had not known that for the past 20 years, the only observation written on the reports of some tens of thousands of bottlings was 'normal'. The furious microbiologist got Ken into a corner, by the lapels of his lab coat, and tried to shake an explanation out of him. Ken blurted out in self-defence that he was just an honest scientist doing his job, reporting exactly all the risks that might at some time develop into a quality problem.

"But that's normal!" screamed the microbiologist, banging Ken's head against the wall, adding, "and don't you forget it!"

Note to file: The time usually comes to every man, at some time or another, to consider surrender. But not when you are having your brains bashed out against a brick wall.

In the back rooms of the lab, I was introduced to a routine that had been going on forever, or so it seemed. In fact, it had been in the 1890s that there was an industry scare of small amounts of arsenic being found in a range of beers across the country. It was eventually traced to faulty production of a widely purchased industrial sugar used in the brewing process, but the stigma remained for some time.

Whilst not involved at the time, Bass suffered in the aftermath, being accused by competitors some 20 years later, in a 'dirty tricks' campaign, of not having got rid of the threat of arsenic in its beers.

The company's response was to initiate arsenic analysis, on a routine basis, on everything that could conceivably contain even the smallest traces of this poison, despite the complete absence of it in the beer. A brainstorming session (I suppose today it would be called a focus group or some such modish name, and therefore much more effective) ended up by identifying the coal used in the open fires of the malt-drying kilns as the only possible entry of arsenic into the brewing process.

Accordingly, routine analysis was initiated of every rail truck of coal coming into the brewery. As I stood in the lab 40 years later, I learnt that arsenic had only ever appeared in one sample, seven years before: the railway truck had been instantly isolated to a disused brewery siding, and negotiations started with the National Coal Board about their contract to provide arsenic-free coal.

As it is impossible to get a representative sample from a truck of solid matter like coal, there started a totally irreconcilable argument, as the Coal Board lab failed to find any trace of arsenic in sample after sample (as did our own lab on repeat samples). Today, the private railway system has long disappeared, as indeed has the National Coal Board: and, presumably, a cheap truck of coal as well, into the hands of some enterprising scrap merchant.

Note to file: It is a good idea to review the effectiveness of your resources from time to time, and to reallocate them accordingly.

Not that one always has the freedom to decide what to do and what not to do with one's resources. In the summer, a large bottle of water used to be delivered to the lab regularly every Monday morning, and it was the chief scientist's job to measure the water's pH (acidity/alkalinity), and to stand by the phone at 10 am precisely, to await the chairman's secretary's bidding for this vital analysis. The full story emerged when Ken was standing in for the great Dr Rainbow, who was away on holiday. Ken had delegated the actual analysis to a young assistant (anyone can measure a pH) and then dutifully stood by the phone at 10am. When 'she in her carpet slippers who shall be obeyed', as she was known locally, failed to recognize Ken's voice, she demanded to know where Dr Rainbow was, as only he was allowed to give her the analysis. Explaining his absence, Ken pointed out that he had been fully briefed only the Friday before, and he had the result on a piece of paper in front of him.

"Are you qualified to give me a pH?" she screamed down the phone.

"I haven't got a Ph.D., if that's what you mean, Miss Holden......"

"I will report this to the chairman immediately", she interrupted, completely missing the point, and, perhaps fortunately, the joke. "If anything goes wrong with his swimming pool this week, you will be held personally responsible!"

Note to file: You must have the confidence to stand up to overwhelming threats and disbelief of your competence in high places.

In 1966, a new concept had been invented for measuring the colour of beer, which is considered rather an important characteristic from the customer's viewpoint, although 20 years earlier Draught Bass was available to publicans in a choice of at least 12 different depths of colour. This led one to believe that colour was either extremely important, or possibly not important at all; one will never find out, and anyway in those days the serious drinker often had his own pewter tankard in his favourite pub: whilst concealing the colour, this was also very handy for avoiding complaints of cloudy beer, which was widespread due to the standards of brewery and pub hygiene of that era.

Until this invention, which was an instrument capable of measuring depth of colour wholly objectively, it was necessary for the human eye to compare the colour of the beer against a selection of coloured transparent discs, which inevitably led to considerable variations of subjective opinion.

I was instructed on the use of this traditional method by a long-serving chemist, who had been in charge of measuring the colour of every beer leaving the brewery for at least a decade. I was surprised at the wide range of colour reported in some of the beers, as the records that I had previously seen in the brewery were contrastingly very consistent.

It turned out that the brewers had their own coloured discs, of which only one seemed to be in use, namely that of the colour that the beer ought to be. However, I was forced to put to the back of my mind such unscientific behaviour by the brewers when, shortly after, the 'colour' chemist discovered that he was colour blind.

Note to file: It is surprising how often a technological advance seems to occur which fulfils a long unfelt need, only to discover that you do actually need it.

At last, I was given a proper quality 'problem' to solve. It had arisen from a meeting of our chairman and the chairman of another brewing group, both directors of British Rail, in the buffet car of a train, when each had ordered a bottle of their own beer. Our new chairman was the first of this great Burton Brewery who had had little experience of the national brewing scene: he had just appeared as a result of our merger with Mitchells and Butlers and had organised, some said bullied, himself into the chairmanship of the new group. So, without any knowledge of the character of his most traditional of Burton beers, he compared it with his 'mediocre' competitor.

He was horrified and embarrassed that his superlative beer had no 'head' (foam) on it, compared with the thick white head on the beer of his companion (later universally nicknamed K9P - the beer, not the chairman). Our chairman had clearly immediately decided that here was his opportunity to make his mark on this new, highly traditional part of his empire. The next day, after 190 years of tradition where flavour of the beer had been paramount over any modish physical characteristic, he issued an instruction that 'with effect from Monday 5th October, all our Burton beers will have a head on them'.

Note to file: There is nothing like keeping your people on their toes.

On being given the task by Sir to participate in the resolution of this dichotomy, I saw immediately that this was the breakthrough for the scientists to contribute to change: and how fortunate (or was it planned?) to have such a young enthusiastic head brewer to conduct brewing trials of such a dramatic, indeed heretical nature.

It was at this stage that I first became involved with consultants, when Sir decided to recruit an American firm of brewing consultants to the investigation team. It has always been said that consultants borrow your watch to tell you the time, then sell it back to you; this proved absolutely true in this case, among the other frustrations and questions that arise from having to open your heart to outsiders, instead of dealing directly with the boss.

As the investigation proceeded, I became increasingly interested in finding some important answers to the whole question of consultancy.

Firstly, why are consultants needed, when you and others on the staff are better qualified on the subject at issue? The initial reaction is that the boss does not trust his staff to solve the problem by themselves, but on second thoughts it is far more likely that it is the boss who does not trust *himself* to lead the team to success.

Secondly, why is a company prepared to pay enormous fees for the advice that it knows it is unlikely to get? Correct answer: the higher the cost of advice, the more valuable is it perceived. And if it fails to come up with the goods, one can claim that the best advice in the world was sought in vain, relieving the team leader of responsibility.

Thirdly, if a consultant claims to be that good at problem solving, why is he a consultant and not practising his skills in the real world, at a salary that he could almost nominate himself? There is no polite answer to that.

Note to file: Consultants obviously have a place in the world, to help those who ought to know better.

Like all insoluble problems - even today there is no brewing process devised to guarantee a good 'head' on beer - a compromise solution was found that got the chairman off our backs, and the matter was conveniently forgotten for ten years. That was when I had to entertain him at the brewery some time after his retirement, and it all came back to me at the sight of his face. Noting that he was in good heart and humour, I reminded him of the stress he had put us under, those many years ago.

"I remember it well," he replied, "and it had an effect, did it not?"

"It must have been important for you to remember" I hazarded.

"You bet it was. Take a tip from me, if you are ever in the position to make a similar order of such importance that it overrides the culture of the company, you will always get the best results if you make it with effect from a Monday!"

Who needs consultants when you have a chairman like that?

*

When in office, the chairman was certainly an awesome figure, with plentiful stories flying around of instant sackings of senior managers for trivial variations from his orders. Thus, it was with some trepidation that I received an invitation from him, to a dinner at the London head office. I learned that these dinners were, in fact, well known in the business world, often being mentioned in the national press as the height of management development technique; not that there were many other techniques with which to compare them in the 1960s.

The ritual was to subject aspiring managers to an intensely intimidating atmosphere, within which they had to know how to behave, and to perform by speaking on a subject of their own choice relevant to the future of the company, in front of all the important directors. Tales abounded of sackings the following morning, despite an undertaking by the chairman that there was no taboo subject matter of any kind.

The method of selection for invitations seemed to me somewhat arbitrary, as how else did I come to be included? I concluded that head office must have taken, each year, all the organization charts of the group, guillotined off the top three inches of each, shuffled them, then divided them into blocks of about 20 invitees to each dinner: certainly, no other explanation seemed possible for such a ragtag of strange people to come together and compete with each other.

Well washed and dressed up to the nines, I found myself sitting next to the group's director of wines, one of the nicest persons I had so far met in this company, who oozed confidence and qualifications in his chosen profession. Wine, I thought, must come a close second to beer as the ultimate social lubricant. He talked me through the wine list that we enjoyed during the meal, inspiring interest from all those around him: in those days every brewery company had an active business in fine wines, some of the best of which, of course, always ended up in the chairman's cellar. Port was not mentioned on the menu; this was surprising, at least until the decanters circulated. When everyone had filled their glasses, the chairman turned to my nearby expert.

"Well, Vincent, what do you make of this port?" he challenged.

Unflustered, Vincent picked up his glass, did all the right things, tasted it, and considered his reply.

"It reminds me of a number of cases that I purchased for you some time ago, chairman. And with this quality, it can only be Dow '45," he stated with uncanny complacency.

"Well done," said the chairman, "I hope you will all enjoy such a rare treat."

I leant over to the man of the moment. "I think I know what I like, but how on earth can you identify wines to such accuracy?" I enquired innocently.

"Take a tip from me," he smiled, "One look at the label is worth 25 years in the trade! I'm glad no one saw me slip into the kitchen during cocktails."

Note to file: Leave nothing to chance when you know that your reputation might be at risk.

The chairman then gave an introductory spiel on the dynamism of the company, including his new plans for diversification, in this case the recent purchase of a mineral water business in Birmingham, which was bringing much synergy into the marketing, sales and distribution of drinks to our licensed house customers. Suddenly, the mood changed.

"Say something, Tibbits," he said, pointing directly at me. Whether it was the crushing shock of being picked first, or the uplift of my unexpected anonymity (who cares if someone called Tibbits gets the sack?), I completely forgot my carefully rehearsed spontaneous observations on company matters, and went into a semi-conscious mode that I had never before experienced.

"I think it wonderful that we are moving forward on diversification, chairman," I heard my voice say, "but if we are already so well set up on mineral waters, why is it that when I order them to be delivered to my home from the brewery depot, the bottles always come with a competitor's label on them?"

"What a good question," thundered the chairman, turning to the director in charge of brewery depots. "What are you going to do about that, Peter?" My concern for unintentionally embarrassing one of the directors present was happily assuaged.

"We know all about that, chairman. It will all be sorted out next week," said Peter.

"Does that answer satisfy you, Tibbits?" enquired the chairman.

"Thank you, chairman," I replied, sinking with relief into oblivion, whilst the others made their own earth-shattering contributions to the future of the company. I did, however, make a mental note to order some mineral waters the following week, if only to appreciate the effectiveness of the director in charge of brewery depots.

Note to file: Always be wary of putting yourself into any situation where you might have to activate mouth before brain, particularly after you got away with it the first time.

When, the following week, I rang to order some mineral waters from the depot to be delivered home, the manager seemed somewhat distraught.

"I'm terribly sorry, Bob," he said, "I don't know what's happened, but the director has issued strict instructions not to supply mineral waters any more."

Note to File: There are many ways to skin a cat including those that you would never think of in 100 years.

This sad state of affairs had its influence on my children

70

mostly; certainly not on my local vicar, who would invariably appear at the door within 48 hours of the company's wagon being spotted from the vicarage. Since there were no company pubs in the area, it was reasonable to assume that my house was the scheduled target for replenishment of alcoholic hospitality. This more than wrote off the benefit of purchase at wholesale prices, but was good for the soul.

Looking back on these events of more than 30 years ago, I am amazed how one took in one's stride the right of staff, of quite lowly seniority, to be able to have their liquid refreshment delivered to their home. Another brownie point for paternalism.

*

Fairly quickly after my arrival in the lab, Cyril Rainbow moved off the scene to run a separate research facility more appropriate to our rapidly expanding group, as more and more breweries came into the fold.

I became, entirely by chance and totally unexpectedly, a proper manager, in charge of quality control in this huge brewing operation.

Note to file: In 90 per cent of cases, promotions are as a result of being accidentally in the right place at the right time. The other 10 per cent is reserved for those with the skill to *get* themselves into the right place at the right time.

CHAPTER 5

CHANGING THE COMPANY CULTURE

During the mid-1960s, mergers between the larger brewing groups continued, whilst smaller companies continued to be bought and aggregated into these massive combines. The largest of these mergers involved the empire originated by Eddie Taylor, by then a nationwide conglomerate of small to medium sized breweries called United Breweries, uniting further with the big London brewers Charrington.

His empire now had 'tied' pubs in sufficient numbers and geographical spread to introduce seriously national beer brands. This did not stop the further opportunity in 1967 to merge his Charrington United Breweries with Bass, Mitchells and Butlers to form Bass Charrington, the largest brewing group in the UK

Four or five other groups were forming in a similar fashion, but none had the presence across the whole of the United Kingdom that Bass Charrington then possessed, with breweries and pubs in Scotland, Wales and Northern Ireland as well as covering all the main English regions. Guinness remained in this major league of national brewery groups, as the only company without the need for ownership of pubs to present its products to the public.

Despite the universal presence of Bass Charrington, which raised comments about 'monopolies' even then (and right through to the turn of the millennium), neither this company, nor any other, ever attained even 25 per cent of the UK beer market; that is, until after the famous beer orders at the start of the 1990s, designed to *reduce* market share of the big brewers. Meanwhile, most countries of the western world were enjoying their beer where the leading brewer held between 40 and nearly 100 per cent of market share, without any government interference whatsoever.

Following their big merger, Bass Charrington set about making the most of their exceptional range of well-known beer brands, included in them the still little known, slow selling lager brand from Canada named Carling Black Label, eventually to become Britain's biggest brand ever. I never saw Eddie Taylor; after this merger, his personal interest in acquisitions necessarily had to fade and it seemed to be left to the marketeers and brewers to develop the day-to-day success of new and existing beer brands.

The 1960s decade was also the age of intense technological development in both brewery and pub to satisfy the increasing sophistication of consumers, which brought the field of quality control directly into the forefront of the production and beer serving processes.

This was not to everyone's taste or pleasure. At the top of the list was the conversion of draught beer from wooden casks into either metal casks or metal kegs, the introduction of large enclosed stainless steel brewery vessels with sterile stainless steel pipework, and efficient clean methods of storing and dispensing beer from the pub cellar to the glass.

*

It is a basic tenet that you cannot control quality until at first you measure it. From this basic truth there had developed over the years three fundamental types of quality control, each development requiring a quantum leap, not in the technology itself but in attitude by the managers of the new technology.

1. Quality reporting:

At its simplest, desirable measurable characteristics are identified, these being usually (or hopefully) features that make the product most acceptable to the consumer. Routine analyses of these characteristics are undertaken, and reported to the production managers, in this case the brewers. The managers then decide themselves what to do with these figures. It is usually too late to take any action on any one result, so one must choose either to ignore it, or to study the figures all together to identify any trends away from the desired quality norms, and then to make the appropriate adjustments to the production process. To be generous towards the traditional head brewers, the use of the latter alternative as their idea of quality 'control' did have a limited use.

2. Quality Control:

True quality control must specify every quality characteristic related to customer acceptance, define acceptable variations from these norms, and to have a system of rejection or reprocessing when these variations are exceeded. And all this must happen before the product leaves the factory. Trends away from acceptability must be corrected routinely as good management practice.

All this seems so obvious today, but not in a world of draught beer when it was in the hands of the publican to present the beer in the best way possible, while it matured and changed in the environment of a poorly-equipped cellar. A typical pub cellar in the 1960s would rely on its natural underground environment in the summer, and a brick on a gas ring in the winter as its temperature control system. In addition, there were only primitive means of cleaning the beer pipes.

It was the move to tamperproof ready-to-serve bright beer pasteurized in the brewery, served through hygienic pipe systems that demanded these new management attitudes.

3. Quality Assurance:

Quality assurance is the in-phrase at the turn of the millennium, as forward-looking manufacturers strive towards perfect quality practices. Quality assurance is perfect if managed perfectly. In effect, if your control system is working faultlessly, it is not necessary to hold your product at the factory until every quality check is complete. You then use your data historically to identify any trends towards a risk situation, and take appropriate corrective action before it can become a problem. For instance, a vital quality check on an export product, which may take five days to complete, should not prevent you despatching it immediately, when you can assure yourself that the product will always be within the limits of acceptability.

However, this idyllic state of affairs must not be confused with ISO 9000 and its homologues, established in the late 1980s as the international system of detailing quality procedures within a process. Although this is a natural companion to quality assurance, it consists of massive manuals of how a company tackles all aspects of its quality performance, but nowhere in these manuals is it required to specify how *well* quality is *actually* controlled. This leaves wide open the opportunity for the incompetent manager to become even more incompetent, as he thinks he is doing a good quality job by simply and mindlessly following these bureaucratic procedures.

Note to file: Consider ISO 9000 as a good example of the triumph of bureaucracy over natural good management practice.

However, back in 1966, the effort was to introduce some natural good management practice, using the best quality control techniques of the day. As explained, the urgency of this was not related to any existing gross deficiency nationally in general beer quality: the variability of draught beers through their lives in pub cellars was well accepted by the consumer, and normally this outweighed any deficiency there might have been in the beer when it left the brewery.

It was the birth of keg beer (chilled, filtered and pasteurized in the brewery, then filled into sterile metal containers) that provided the novel concept to the public of the consistent 'perfect' pint of draught beer every time. This would naturally require much more carefully controlled quality, because if the beer was not consistently perfect when it left the brewery, how could one claim that it should be consistently perfect in the pub?

The first keg beers had begun to appear, slowly, during the 1950s. After lengthy experimentation and development of the technique, Sir took the decisive step in the Bass breweries in Burton to go into full production. Not that the brewers were in unanimous agreement that their traditional art form was going to need scientists to interfere with their new-found sophisticated technology.

In our case, the new head brewer, as always, came to the rescue. Once Arthur saw his opportunity to command precision quality in this new type of beer, there was no stopping him; within weeks, a 24-hour laboratory was set up in the brewery, and tight quality specifications established.

Note to file: The best way of selling an idea is not to sell it but to get the receiver to want to buy. Put another way, get the receiver of an idea to believe that he thought of it first.

Arthur then assembled his troops to inform them of the new quality control system. This involved the brewers having to hold the beer at varying stages of the process until the lab had reported whether the beer was fit to proceed or not. In the latter case, the duty brewer had only two options - to reprocess the beer into specification or to summon Arthur himself to decide what to do. As if to offset the indignity of a lab technician now having the power to stop the brewers from making their own decisions, Arthur had appointed himself the sole arbiter between the conflicting pressures on quality, and the need to keep the warehouse full of beer for the next day's deliveries.

I suggested that a week's trial might be in order before confirming this change of power, so as to get used to the idea of increased reprocessing and its effect on production; but Arthur would have none of it. No, there was nothing better than the next Monday to make a real live start. As the meeting dispersed, I said to Arthur that, on current quality performance, he must expect his brewery output to come to a grinding halt on Monday morning.

"Splendid!" cried Arthur, "It's the only way they'll all learn that we're serious!"

"You'll be learning too, Arthur. Your brewers think that this new discipline is impossible to achieve," I replied. "And you've got 24-hour shifts on, so they'll be screaming down the phone at you all night when there's no beer to load on to the wagons."

"They jolly well won't," came the riposte, "I shall be out in the trade most nights next week, so they'll have to resolve their mistakes themselves!"

Come Monday, the brewers succeeded as normal in filling all the available tanks, but only with beer that needed further quality adjustments, thus leaving none ready to be filled into kegs. No, Arthur was not going to allow anything to be packaged that was the slightest bit out of acceptability. So the brewery came to its inevitable halt.

However, by Friday, as Arthur continually forced the brewers to get the beer 'right' to the new standards, this 'impossible' discipline had become fully implemented and accepted by all as a major step forward into the future of beer quality. And all it cost to crack this tradition and culture was a weekend of overtime to catch up on the production lost during the week.

Note to file: Paternal chucking into the deep end seems a good way of achieving a new discipline, style and culture. However, for the fastest results, the chucker-in needs to be close, involved and committed - and big.

*

Note to file: Confirmation received that Monday *is* a great day for changing a company's culture.

It was around this time that the great Bass traditions came into full contact with the completely different management style of the other half of the new Bass Charrington outfit.

The thought of amalgamating a seemingly tough commercial outfit with our highly traditional company was somewhat daunting to us, and therefore had to be approached with some caution, particularly as *their* brewing HQ was in the capital city of our great country.

Shortly after the merger, Arthur happened to be in the sample store showing off a brand new suit, being in a tweed of pattern and colours that fitted perfectly his personality - big, loud and bright. Everyone thought he looked magnificent. Suddenly, Sir swept in and directed his commanding voice at Arthur.

"Arthur, I want you to represent the brewery at the first brewers' meeting with the new group in their London headquarters the day after tomorrow. We will need to create a good impression, so you had better get a new suit; we don't want you going down there looking like a country bumpkin."

As Sir swept out, we suitably encouraged poor deflated Arthur about his sartorial taste, and advised him on an appropriate dress code applicable to this journey into the unknown. Arthur departed splendidly to London wearing a dark pin stripe suit with rolled umbrella and bowler hat, looking exactly like Odd Job.

*

Note to file: Adaptability in dress for all occasions is a vital factor in creating a good impression and influencing people.

The greatest change that swept into our Bass part of the group was the introduction of the other's system of management controls, both financial and operational. Phrases such as management accounting, labour cost control, loss control, budgeting, capital control, work study, to mention just a few, started to be bandied about, and a whole new department of accountants and management services suddenly appeared. And a personnel department to be reckoned with as well.

At the start, everyone was well motivated about all the money that was going to be saved by these dozens of people, but it did not take too long to realize that they were simply there to help the 'doers' do all the saving. Another disadvantage, of course, was that we did not have any experience of a past financial performance to compare with. As far as I was aware, the only previous financial 'control' over the brewers had been a half-yearly mention from the accountants; this usually consisted of an observation that too much beer seemed to be being brewed that did not end up being sold, so it would be better if less duty-paid beer was wasted during the production process.

The answer to that was that HM Customs and Excise had always given an excise duty 'discount' allowance of 6 per cent to all breweries, in return for average process losses known to be typically about 6 per cent; and since excise duty represented at least threequarters of the value of a beer-in-process, the brewers felt rather unmotivated to do much about reducing wastage, as they were effectively being 'repaid' for it anyway. No one appeared to have worked out that, even if *no* duty-paid beer was lost, one *still* got the 6 per cent discount.

Note to file: If all competitors receive the same rate of discount, in perpetuity, then logical analysis must conclude that no way can it be a discount at all. If you have any doubts about this, think it through. Crafty buggers, these civil servants.

Personally, I was more than content to stand back, in the safe haven of a laboratory service difficult to define in efficiency terms, and watch all these management controls being forced onto, to say the least, a reluctant, sceptical brewery.

Sadly, my distance from such excitement was not to be for long.

*

The management stir-up caused by the huge merger had led Sir to assume new responsibilities, which allowed him to put Arthur in charge of the whole brewery in Burton. As soon as this was organised, Sir went down with an ailment requiring a good many weeks of hospital and recuperation. Delegating from his hospital bed, he gave Arthur a go at his own job, and asked me if I would like to try running the brewery.

Always anxious to please anyone, I found myself in the melee of trying to make sense of these new wonderful management control systems. Every day piles of paper would arrive on my desk for attention, for close study and for appropriate action. Thirty five years is a long time ago to recall detail, but as one example I can remember weekly labour cost control sheets, listing all the hours worked by every man, divided between the different types of hours worked at different pay rates, prepared by a bank of clerks in the management services separtment.

Where was the *control* in these figures? The brewers and I had nothing to compare them with; they came out long after it was possible to trace back any apparent oddities; and any future change in employment policy would be for other reasons, coming through other (then non-existent) means and channels.

But the figures were clearly important, because copies also had to be sent to the new headquarters in London, but with no feedback on how they were to be controlled. They were, in fact, only labour cost *reports*,such as the misnamed quality *control* reports of yesteryear. It was from here that I confirmed my most important lessons on management information reporting:

Note to file: Do not confuse information with knowledge. It becomes knowledge when you know what to do with it, and then *want* to do it. And only when you have done it, does it become know-how.

Note to file: The contents and tools of management information seldom reflect the importance indicated by their heading or title. But if they are any good, one day they will. For instance, how many decades did it take for word processors to be able to process words?

As I was experiencing the same frustrations with all the other similar reports, I decided to visit Sir in hospital in case he was worried about the brewery. But all he asked was if I had any specific problems.

"I can only say, Sir, that I have few ideas on how to cope with and act appropriately on all the vast amount of bumf that comes in every day," I ventured.

"Simple. Do what I do, Bob," he replied with a glint in his eye. "Give yourself a black mark if by 9.30 in the morning your waste paper basket isn't at least three quarters full."

This was my introduction to what I assumed to be the authorized company style of management. Two months later, Sir arrived back, and it fell to my lot to thank Arthur's secretary (who had worked for Sir for several years before) for the wonderful help she had been in keeping me on the right lines.

"Thank you", she replied, "actually it has been a very nice time for me, and the brewery generally, to have a different style of getting things done. But I hope you won't mind me saying that you have exactly the same fault as Sir. Every day, I had to go through your waste paper basket and pull out all the essential information!"

"Oh!" I cried, "how awful. I am so sorry. But do tell me; what have you done with it all?"

"I filed it, of course. Is there anything else that you think I ought to have done with it?"

Note to file: One must always try to find out what is the right thing to do with what others think is essential information. Meanwhile, carry on doing what *you* think is right.

*

Shortly after my return to the lab, Sir decided that I should go on a 12-week executive development course at a well-known business school. This involved me in completing an application form, the prime question being 'Why do you want to attend this course?' Thinking that 'because I have been told to' would probably not be the expected reply, and as there was almost half a page of space requiring to be filled, I had to rack my brains for suitable things to say.

Eventually, I sent the form back for Sir to authorize and send off, but he first summoned me to inform me that it was *not* intended that I should return from the course with the intention of being able to take over *his* job. Much abashed, and reluctant to admit that that was what I thought the school would probably want to read, I retired quickly, and in the rush forgot to ask what the true reason should have been.

Some weeks before the course, an enormous parcel of homework arrived, consisting largely of an elementary course in accountancy. Hooray, at last I was going to be able to penetrate the mysteries of this profession, find out how useful accountants are, and be able to talk to them on equal terms. All this on top of becoming several jumps ahead of my Bass peers on all subjects of management.

Note to file: There is nothing like a little bit of ambition in your psyche. But be careful how you show it.

It is important to recognize that, at the end of the 1960s, organised management development barely existed in most companies. The luckiest students were those attending the very few postgraduate MBA courses in business schools, turning out small numbers of bright young people with inflated egos and an incomprehensible vocabulary of new management terms, enough to impress (if not flummox) any traditional managing director.

These MBA courses had therefore easily established a powerful academic status, able to fuel both highly paid strategy (and such like) departments within companies, and a wealth of management consultancies, manned by those full of theory but hardly enough experience of real-life management to write on a postage stamp.

It took companies a long time to start sorting the sheep from the goats in this new world, but at least it kept unemployment down for a bit. It was with this background that I arrived for my three-month induction into modern management thinking and practice.

*

The first thing to say about a long high level course, on any subject broadly related to your job, is not to be disappointed if you find no more than 20 per cent of the material to be of much direct use in improving your own future job performance. The remaining 80 per cent should be used as far as possible to pick up key elements only, enough to be able to discuss these matters on equal terms with your appropriate specialist service functions.

Also, whatever your personal opinion of your own company's management performance, a quick assessment of your course peers will make you realise what a great, fantastic company it is that you work for. However, this was unlikely to apply to the managers of nationalised industries, well represented on my course, who appeared to be there in rotation for the purposes of using up some training budget, at a rate necessary to prove to the world their industries' commitments to management development.

Note to file: When cloistered with a bunch of inferior equals, reward yourself and your company by flying its flag as hard as you can.

In the late 1960s formal quantifiable management techniques were coming into vogue, hence it was inevitable that the main contender of the day, Management By Objectives (MByO), would be well aired on this course. And so it was, but by a professor with wide academic experience on organizational behaviour. Thus was introduced a psychological discipline into the cosy life of UK managers, who up till then had been managing (they thought) perfectly well by the seat of their pants.

MByO may not be entirely familiar to the modern young manager, as it has been surpassed many times by variants, each of which made a fortune for their consultant inventors of new catch-phrases, each sounding even more impressive than the last, but in fact saying exactly the same thing - 'pay us to show you how to be better managers by measuring and targeting manager performance'.

There must have been something in it all, because as I was retiring 20 years or so later, I started to hear 'Main Purpose of Job', 'KRAs' (Key Result Areas), 'KPIs' (Key Performance Indicators) and other essential jargon of original MByO being bandied about, as if someone had thought up yet another wonderful system for improving management performance.

Note to file: Beware management techniques that have undergone so much change and development that they have arrived back at the starting gate.

Obviously, that 'Note to file' had to have been written in the 1990s, but in no way was I cynical about MByO at the time; far from it, I was all ears to find out what it was all about from the mouth of an open-minded expert.

I recall a long diatribe explaining the actual mechanics of setting up and implementing MByO, as it was the professor's duty so to do. During this I was turning over in my mind that, if a manager is going to be appraised and rewarded for his performance against measurable objectives, e.g. profit, output, machine efficiencies etc. (which I felt a good manager should be doing naturally anyway, without having to set up a massive bureaucracy), what is the feeble manager going to do about his *unquantifiable* responsibilities; for example, personnel relations, communication, and all the other things that motivate his staff and workers. Possible answer: he will pay even less attention to them, whilst he gets the whip out to his workers to achieve his efficiency targets (and thus his bonus).

As I started to worry, the professor gave the whole class his own, similar reservations about implementation of MByO, except in certain circumstances. These included a clear, relevant corporate strategy as the essential engine to drive MByO from the top down through the management layers of the company. Unfortunately, at that moment the bell rang for coffee break, and we were left to work out for ourselves what on earth corporate strategy meant (it *was* the 1960s). But at least it was something to remember and use at the appropriate occasion, should it arise. And it did, a lot sooner than expected.

*

The course droned on as we became familiar with the world of accountants, which made me want more and more to do a job that involved actually dealing with some real ones.

A long session on organizational behaviour was my first experience of having my soul opened up to analysis. Here was the new world of psychometric testing, ready to explode into companies as essential tools for recruitment and selection for promotion. It was not pleasant to find out whether one was X (achievement oriented = nasty) or Y (people oriented = nice) or whatever in-between, which seemed to be the state of the art at that time; but no one seemed to offer any suggestions of what to do about whatever you were.But what an opportunity for consultants to start inventing all kinds of long-winded variants, with interpretations that ideally defy sensible comprehension: and the more esoteric the analysis, the more money they were likely to make out of it.

The first of these tried out on me was to categorize one's management style in crystal clear terms, ranging from grades of 'dictator' at one extreme to 'deserter' at the other. It may not be surprising that the majority of young dynamic managers, particularly those who had to manage people to get results, came out as 'benevolent dictators'.

Note to file: It is said by some that the ideal form of government is a democratic dictatorship. Perhaps this idea comes from industry, where it appears that the nicer the manager running a one-man committee, the better the results.

In my group, one man came out as a 'compromiser', to everyone else's amusement when the consultant said that never in his experience had this happened to him before. At a convenient break we asked the unfortunate if he really thought that he was a compromiser.

"Well......" he started, clearly having problems getting his grey cells round the question. Eventually out came the answer. "Well....er.....yes and no."

Note to file: There really is something going for this psychometric testing business.

Sadly, I never saw the results for managers of any of the nationalized industries.

*

As the course ran its course, I was delighted to receive a letter from the company offering me the job of running a number of breweries in the group for a couple of years, whilst they finished building a brand new enormous brewery in the north, at Runcorn. The real stimulation to me came from the fact that these breweries came from the 'other' side of the merged group, hence the opportunity to find out exactly how their management control systems should really work.

My meeting with the breweries' boss of the north was welcoming and stimulating. The job was to keep five breweries running, until the new big brewery could take over their production, and then to close them. I thought this quite a useful start to senior management because, in the event of a major managerial calamity in a plant due to close anyway, maybe it would be quickly forgotten.

"And by the way, Bob, we will be introducing Management By Objectives in a couple of months," he offered as extra stimulation.

"That's fine, Peter," I replied, "but I'll first need to see the corporate strategy to focus my objectives."

As his eyes seemed to start glazing over, Peter (what a joy it was on the 'other' side not having to call your boss 'sir') mumbled something about getting hold of it, then coming back to me. He never did, and what was the point anyway of setting up a complex bureaucracy of objectives, when the main one was to shut everything down.

Note to file: Making one's efforts a priority must be a key managerial function, to concentrate on the most important things of the moment. But with the arrival of the science of time management, will everyone be spending their time planning it?

CHAPTER 6

CRISIS MANAGEMENT

By 1970, most of the big brewing companies were starting to modernize their breweries, some with big new ones to replace the many unwanted smaller ones that were purchased solely for their pubs. Despite the substantial efforts of the large brewers to become even larger and to evade marauders from outside, this did not stop Grand Metropolitan taking over Watney Mann, and Imperial Tobacco taking over Courage in the first two years of the decade.

The brewing world was never going to be the same again as outsiders thought that they saw means of getting better value out of pub assets (forget offices and breweries – the pubs constitute virtually all the 'value' of a large, vertically-integrated brewing company).

It was a time of serious industrial unrest, as ultra left wing organizations were starting to take a grip on the nation as a whole. Bass Charrington had started to build its huge brewery, capable of producing half of the group's output; it was to be at Runcorn, the up and coming new town of the north. Unsurpassable efficiency would include national distribution of the beer by the containerized system being introduced by British Rail, considered to be the future answer to traffic congestion in our small island.

To alleviate fears of possible labour disruption in an area unfamiliar to Bass, trades unions were approached at very senior level, which promised co-operation to ensure a peaceful construction and startup. Say no more.

*

It was a typically cold and dank January day in 1970 when I arrived at the Manchester headquarters of the company that ran the pubs, the beer distribution and the free trade selling in the north west region. Although our numerous breweries, spread around the country, were cosily tucked into their own separate production company, those out in the sticks had their routine administration provided by these regional companies. So one of these was to be my home base for the two years of keeping the five breweries going, while my boss spent most of his time building the new brewery.

Greeted warmly by the outgoing brewery manager of the five breweries, he pointed to a metallic drawer arrangement in the corner of the office:

"That's the filing cabinet, I think, but there's only one thing you really need," he said, pulling open the bottom drawer of the desk. It revealed a toilet roll.

"There's never any in the loo down the corridor," he explained. "Now I'll introduce you to your secretary, then the executive mess, then I'll be off to my new job."

Note to file: When thrown in at the deep end by your predecessor, don't panic. The chances are that the operation is so well delegated that it has been running perfectly well without him.

To start with, most of the five breweries each had about 30 employees, all of whom had been told that their plants were to be closed. I had so much to learn about personnel policy in this tricky scenario, which would become increasingly sensitive as closure times approached. On top of this was my burning desire to make use of the sophisticated accounting and efficiency systems presented to us by our new merger partner.

People were obviously the first priority. Quite naturally, I expected to find demotivated, gloomy workforces in the breweries. Although it was known that every employee would be given the chance to apply for a job in the new brewery, it had been made clear from the start that the interest would be minimal. For some reason, the prospect of moving house and home to Runcorn did not seem to be particularly appealing at that time. However, in complete contrast to expectations, the breweries, with one exception, were running very smoothly.

All these breweries had been family businesses sold to our big corporation, and the current ease of management of them seemed to be in direct proportion to the previous owners' direct interest in the business and welfare of the employees under their charge. The one exception was inevitably in a large city, where trade union traditions and disciplines are most easily developed and sustained (in this case Manchester). In fact, the announcement of the closure simply provided an opportunity to create even more mayhem than already existed, not only in the brewery, but in the dray fleet deliveries to the pubs as well. Not that 'even more mayhem' made all that much difference, there being so little time left to fit in much more.

Elsewhere, the relative calm provided me with potential havens in which to learn how to use the management techniques and controls, then so excitingly new to me. Firstly, I was presented with my first monthly operating statements for each of the five breweries, which I was so eagerly awaiting. The fact that they were six weeks late did not immediately ring any alarm bells. They contained hundreds of expenditure figures compared with budgets, together with invaluable figures of how efficiently (or otherwise) the beer had been brewed: in fact, all the vital information for a new, eager, dynamic manager like myself to take to his head brewers to analyze, seek explanations and devise action plans.

However, before forcing my presumed superior comprehension upon them, I realized that I had better check first my own full understanding of these statements with the chief accountant. Thus began my long and fruitful relationship with this mysterious profession.

My phone call was well received, with the offer of an appointment four weeks later, being the earliest time available in his busy schedule.

"But the statements are already six weeks out of date." I pleaded, to no avail.

Four weeks later, I took my then ten-weeks-out-of-date documents to his office, was politely received and asked what questions I had.

"To start with," I opened, "I want to be certain how you calculate and keep separate the various efficiency variances, for instance the excise duty variance from the....."

"Good heavens, Bob," interjected the accountant, "You aren't expecting to read anything into these figures, are you?"

Note to file: Think twice before referring to *all* accountants as mysterious, or any other adjective that might imply devious creativity. Some seem to be disarmingly straightforward and honest.

Beyond this grip that the accountants had over brewery performance, the brewers themselves also had to report some weekly efficiency figures to the production company headquarters in London, a set-up that I had yet to experience. All I knew was that it contained no-one from the Bass side of the merged companies, and that its motto was sarcastically spoken of as 'we're from headquarters; we're here to help you'. This was an honour that I had previously thought to be traditionally reserved for personnel departments.

This was a far more dangerous scenario than the local reporting of the financial performance, because these were production experts monitoring activities of direct influence on production efficiencies. For instance, the amount of beer lost in processing (representing potentially large amounts of excise duty down the drain) had to be reported weekly as a percentage to two decimal places, despite most beer being held in large ungauged tanks, making it impossible to take stock of volumes of beer to within one hundredth of that accuracy. This fact in no way inhibited critical analysis of every figure, risking weekly career-threatening thundering over the phone in the event of any losses reported as higher than a set target limit. Just occasional repetition of this sin gave rise to a 'helpful' visit from an expert, which was an event to be avoided at all costs.

It was immediately evident to me that the laid-down methods for measuring waste were so inaccurate, that only an averaging of the weekly figures over at least a two-monthly period would produce anything like a meaningful figure. Fortunately, the brewers had long ago twigged this, and had been keeping 'kitties' of losses to add to or subtract from their calculation, so as to submit a weekly figure within a range unlikely to attract undesirable attention from HQ.

Note to file: In most circumstances, you can fool all of the people some of the time; but to be really clever, just fool the right people all the time. But where is the long-term satisfaction in that?

These initial, rather saddening experiences at least had the benefit of raising my sympathy for my predecessor's vagueness regarding the contents of his filing cabinet, and further enhancing my own appreciation of the selective value of the waste paper basket in effective management.

I also became inspired by a desire to take hold of this theoretically excellent system of financial control, and to try to make it work usefully in the real world. I did not realize, at the time, what a challenge this was to be. It soon resolved itself into four separate, concurrent phases:

1. To get the accountants to understand why the system, as set up, needed to be adapted to practical working conditions, in order to produce useful, actionable data. This took ten years.
2. To get the information produced on time, i.e., before it was too late to do anything about it. This took 15 years.

3. To get the brewery managers to set, and thereby commit themselves to all their own budgets and efficiency targets. This took 20 years.

4. To redesign the information in a format that made it the most comprehensible and useful to the managers, rather than for some esoteric use by the accountants. This was never achieved.

Note to file: You may be able to take a horse to water and make it drink, but it is a lot more difficult to take a dinosaur and make it think. But do maintain good personal relations with the accountants. It won't necessarily do the operation much good, but some of them are actually quite fun, particularly at their leaving parties.

Looking back now on this pathetic performance, the cause had to lie in the almost insuperable hurdles related to the separate existence of what are best described as 'doers' and 'undoers' in any large manufacturing organization. In the case of a brewery, the 'doers' are the brewers and the operators who make the beer, the 'undoers' being the service functions, including personnel, financial and administration. The plant engineers are a separate proud breed, sitting on the fence, getting the best out of being either doers or undoers depending on the tasks of the moment.

'Undoer', of course, can have a supplementary definition, namely those who undo all the good that everyone else is trying to achieve. Fortunately, this type is relatively rare and normally confined to personnel departments (now, of, course, known universally as human resources, which makes them much more relevant). But the type continues to exist, being readily identifiable in the event of crass disasters.

Inevitably, all these non-productive people, whether on site or in a remote ivory tower HQ, have to fight for their places and relative status in the organization, whilst obviously being pretty dependent for their salary on efficient output of beer through the brewery gates. Their most popular self-promoting technique seems to be to make their expertise available to the 'doers' in the most convoluted manner possible, thus making themselves seemingly indispensable through incomprehensibility, and who take the gamble that the 'doers' are unwilling to admit that they are too thick to understand what they are saying.

I often used to try to get service people to talk openly about their contribution to the production team effort; that is, until I asked the chief engineer of a large brewery if he was able to summarize his own contribution, in a single sentence. "That's easy", he replied, without a moment's hesitation. "I design, I order, I install and I commission brewing equipment for the brewers to break, and then I mend it".

*

Note to file: Always try to involve your service functions in a feeling of collective involvement and responsibility for the success of the operation. It might happen one day.

Meanwhile, the problems of just keeping the five breweries going were occupying everyone's minds, whilst the waste paper basket became an increasingly useful administrative tool. Most worrying were serious delays being experienced in the construction of the new Runcorn brewery, the site having been targeted by left wing activists as one of several major building projects across the country – so much for the promises, indeed the power of trades unions to control the militants. The intention seemed to be to demonstrate the ability to inhibit all large industrial development in Britain: how this was going to further the interests of the British working man remained a mystery to me,

At the same time, I was told that one of the unions' north west organisers was openly boasting that, as soon as the Runcorn brewery was irrecoverably committed to its opening, he would be able to hold the company to ransom and be the first union in the country to screw a basic wage of £100 per week for its members. Thus did I learn my first lesson about dealing with trades unions, about which perhaps our own high level people might have been a little more streetwise.

As the situation at Runcorn got worse and worse, a fire destroyed most of the new warehouse on the site, resulting in my two-year sojourn being immediately extended to at least three years. This was far too long a delay for the brands' marketing plan, which had been to launch a new beer in the whole northern commercial TV region when the new brewery had been expected to open. Thus I was faced with not only delaying the brewery closures, but also being required to brew the new beer in some of these old plants. All this led to complications beyond all conceivable expectations.

In the Manchester brewery, we started experiencing unusual happenings, over and above the normal never-ending demands of reward for the slightest change in working practices, or a request for any form of initiative from the brewery operators. Strangely, the traditional trade union practice of trying to negotiate every little change only in exchange for money started spreading into demands for essential creature comforts such as colour TVs in the operators' rest rooms.

Note to file: It is useless to think that giving in to ludicrous demands will resolve an issue. There are always endless supplies of new, even more ludicrous ones.

To put into perspective some of the occurrences that we encountered, it is necessary to explain that there are one or two things that a brewer must expect to experience, at the very most, only once in a lifetime. Among these can be included events such as a royal visit, or finding a dead cat floating on top of a vat of fermenting beer. We had two (of the latter) in one week.

Cats were necessary employees of breweries in those days,

to keep the rodent population down in the area of grain handling plant, and they normally have the wit to avoid the lethal carpet of carbon dioxide gas immediately above a vessel of fermenting beer. However, such events were occurring in just sufficient numbers nationally to justify the inclusion, in one of the master brewer examinations, of the question: 'describe the course of action that you would take if, when in charge of the night shift, you found a dead cat floating on the surface of a vessel of fermenting beer'.

'Pick it up by the tail and throw it into the boiler when no one is looking' scored no marks, as did 'exactly the same as if I had found a dead excise officer floating in the beer'. Correct answer: get a (live) excise officer out of bed to agree that the contaminated beer is eligible for repayment of excise duty; agree the volume of beer in the vessel and take samples for confirmation of original gravity; dispose of cat; arrange to telephone the sewage works to agree time and speed of running to drain (fermenting beer is one of the world's strongest organic effluents to treat); run the beer to waste under supervision of an excise officer at the agreed time and rate; clean and sterilize all plant that has been in contact.

This painstaking costly task would have been quite enough to stimulate any disgruntled potential saboteur to try his hand: in fact, the second cat was found, most unusually, at the *bottom* of the vat, thus contaminating all the tanks into which the beer had been blended. If it really was a saboteur, he must have had acute satisfaction from embarrassing the company's finances by a factor of at least four times.

As time crept on, the stalwart experienced brewers held the fort magnificently, rarely lacking beer ready to leave the brewery. Whether the dray fleet was there to take it away was another matter altogether, beyond rational thought and reason. At times, frustration led to talk of shutting the brewery early, as a means of pressurizing the shop stewards into maintaining some kind of order, and keep employment going for the members as long as possible. This evil management threat was neatly scotched by the shop stewards: they demanded immediate closure!

Note to file: Beware talking openly of any management action that you might or might not want to make use of in the future. Whichever way, you will surely be outmanoeuvred. This is because open honest management (which we all like to think we practice?) stands little chance against animal cunning.

It was at this stage that the full significance of what was going on came to me. The Runcorn brewery construction was clearly under the influence of purely politically-led industrial action; but here in Manchester we had the draymen (with secure jobs) continually holding the company to ransom, and 30 or so operators in the brewery, mostly family men to whom an 18-month extension was a godsend.

This could only be manipulation by a couple of shop stewards, who seemed to have no other motive than to further their own interests within a tight union circle. Whatever these interests might have been, one thing was certain; no matter what happened to the others, they themselves would be able to obtain well-paid employment elsewhere with no difficulty, to continue their obstructive doings at the expense of a fresh lot of union members and their companies. This degree to which local unions can be a power unto themselves I found profoundly disturbing, having come from companies where biting the hand off the source of one's livelihood was far from being on anyone's agenda.

Equally frustrating in these disputes and wildcat actions was the involvement of the company itself. On their agenda were the financial consequences, whether loss of profit or knock-on effects on other company operations, the latter necessarily involving HQ personnel. Whatever support the company initially gave to making a stand against ludicrous demands, it inevitably led at some time to an instruction to negotiate a compromise (give in). This would invariably arrive at a moment of most embarrassment to us on the ground, giving the shop stewards even more power to create mayhem the next time. This pattern of industrial relations problems was often backed up by local shop stewards taking a levy from members' weekly pay packets as a 'strike fund', to be repaid during the weeks of their drawn-out organized 'disputes'.

This type of frustration must have been prevalent in many industries, particularly where a sale lost one day cannot be recouped the next. This is true of pubs with no beer, even more so with the newspaper industry: when things got so bad there, that particular type of mayhem had to be resolved by a decisive strategy of enormous proportions, the financial risk of which had to be borne by the shareholders. There are few other examples of such courage that can be quoted: in the end, certainly for us, the short term demands of the financial world on company performance seemed to outweigh all other considerations.

*

Note to file: Never underestimate the role of trades unions and the City in leaving Britain behind in the economic progress of post-war Europe.

As the time drew nearer to the brewery closure, brewers and supervisors were moving one by one to be trained for the new brewery, making it necessary, at any cost, to rearrange minor responsibilities among those remaining. One of these tasks was to make the necessary entries in the excise book during the evening shift, which required, in fact, only two simple figures. I approached the best operator on that shift to tempt him to undertake these entries.

"Sorry, Guv", he replied. "I ain't got a GCE in maths". Obviously, he had been instructed not to co-operate. At that moment, the brewery bookie's runner (my God, I thought, how do these things come about?) rushed up to him. "Hey, Joe, four of your six mixed trebles have come up at 3 to 1, evens, 10 to 1 and 7 to 2", he announced, slapping him on the back.

"Blimey", cried Joe, "that means I've won £37.70", which wasn't a bad week's wage in those days. Thus I experienced yet another facet of the power of trades unions over the members; namely, the determination to maintain the 'them and us' conflict to their own advantage, at the expense of any opportunity that might arise for the brighter operators to advance themselves. It was to be nearly 20 years before seeing much real progress towards full democracy in industry, if that meant making use of everybody's abilities to the full.

Eventually, the time came to make a final check that none of the operators wished to apply for a job in the new brewery. Not surprisingly, they all applied to a man, under orders from the shop stewards. Although we knew that nobody wanted to go and that they knew that we knew, we knew that they knew that we knew that it was all a time-wasting trick. But, as always, the management commitment had to be honoured. In accordance with the rules of the game, the personnel manager of the new brewery arranged interviews for all of them over two days, whilst being fully aware of the union stance.

Following the interviews, each operator received a letter regretting that he had insufficient experience to work in such a modern brewery, employing so much new technology. The following week, the same personnel manager placed an advertisement in the local newspaper: 'Operators wanted for a new brewery in Runcorn - no previous experience required'.

Note to file: It is always better to assume that your personnel department will cock things up. It makes it that much more agreeable on the occasions when it doesn't.

In the end, the final day came. Judging it advisable to keep everyone off the brewery site, the company bussed them off to a huge surprise party at a local working men's club. Unfortunately their colleagues on the beer delivery fleet were on strike, so there was none of their own beer to drink, but this did not stop them leaving, eight hours later, in an appropriately inebriated state. The last man out caught the attention of the head brewer and asked him what he was going to do about the fish. His astonished enquiry of 'what fish?' received the response, 'didn't you know there's a trout farm in the water tank on the roof of the brewery?'

Note to file: Be ever aware of alternative profitable uses for your company's equipment.

Through a strange kind of inverted sentimentality, I purchased the brewery's rather pretty weather vane from the scrap merchant contracted to clear the site, and installed it in the skyline of my home village. It worked well for a week or so before getting permanently stuck. Careful directional analysis revealed that the pointer was aimed in perpetuity directly at its original home.

Game, set and match to the bastards, I thought.

*

It was at this time that I came into direct contact with interests and activities within the beerage. The son and heir of Lord Gretton (as in Bass, Ratcliff & Gretton, one of the old names of the company) arrived in the Manchester office to provide management services support to the regional operations. This was the era when the descendants of the original lordships were fading out of the picture of a modernizing brewing industry, except for those with evident management skills, who were prepared to work their way through the organization on merit alone.

The Hon John was a supreme example of one of those. I had met his father several times at the research foundation 15 years before, where he showed the amateur enthusiasm in scientific development typical of the titled brewery owners during the previous century. Less typical perhaps was his apparent ownership of only one suit, of country-style tweed somewhat heavily stained; this was a genetic trait passed through to his son.

In between running his stately home, he commanded the company's purchasing and production of barley and malt. He was a true doyen of the industry and had acquired much status and respect in the brewing and agricultural world by mounting an annual mobile exhibition at all the major agricultural shows, encouraging farmers to grow the best barley varieties for beer brewing.

In the 1920s he had made his mark after *his* father had made some innocent but, to some people, disparaging remarks in the House of Lords about Ireland. The net result was the immediate rejection of Bass beers from Irish pubs, and he sent his son to appease the publicans and to collect the money owing from those who had refused further supplies.

Life was very stylish in those days, when Bass representatives travelled only by coach and horses, and business was carried out in an equally gentlemanly manner. To his total surprise, the publican who was thought the most likely to refuse to pay up seemed well appeased by his approaches, and calmly wrote out the requisite cheque. However, on the way to the bank he noted that the cheque had been made out to 'Bass, Ratcliff and that other bastard'. It is not recorded whether he presented the cheque to the bank as a get-back on his father or to put an end to his own miserable detachment to the Emerald Isle, but the honoured cheque remained framed in all its glory in the company's offices for decades afterwards.

Outside these activities, he opened his stately home (Stapleford, now a posh hotel/conference centre) to the public, with the entertainment theme of trips in models of famous ships on the lake and narrow-gauge steam trains around the park. In true Bass paternalistic style he would invite members of brewery staff and their families to a free visit, but had the habit of inviting them at the end of the trip into his greenhouses to pick a plant to take home, then charge them for it. He was a truly historic Bass man.

His son, the Hon John, with whom I was to enjoy being associated for a year or two in Manchester, was entirely different, apart from the family paucity in the matter of male clothing; his suit was shiny to the point of it almost looking as though it was meant to be. When he had been on one of Arthur's team-building weekend trips to Wales he lost the sole of a shoe; after stumbling his way to a shoe shop, he tried to buy a single shoe. He admitted that he had never before been alone into a shoe shop (or indeed most kinds of clothes store) and therefore had no idea that they were only sold in pairs.

My time with him was a critical period in his life. His father had not been in the best of health and so he had the burden of preparing himself to take over the title and the stately home as and when nature demanded. He had already taken over all the land surrounding the stately home, constituting thousands of acres and the appropriate number of villages, and there was still a little time to go to achieve the seven-year period required for avoidance of death duties. He told me that his one mission in life was to preserve the estate for the next generation, despite the ravages of post-war taxation on the landed gentry, which seemed to have landed him with their classic problem, namely to be asset rich but cash poor.

His first major step towards his next generation was to get married and to buy a house. He judged it wise to purchase a house that would be readily saleable in the event of his inheritance and chose a new estate house in the village where I was living. With his appointment to the Manchester office I was therefore able to enjoy his company both at work and while travelling. Not a week went by without some bizarre and entertaining tale of his struggle to keep up with his steadily increasing responsibilities; nevertheless his superb analytical mind, sense of humour and surprising comprehension of how the common herd really lives (so long as it did not actually *involve* him) invariably allowed him to win through to each successive new challenge.

His first great challenge, of course, had been his advance inheritance of the estate's land, to which he applied great logic, in appreciating that the farmland needed far more expertise and leadership than he or his family were competent to give to it. A typical experience of his own land had been to go shooting and to be booted off by an angry tenant to whom his father had apparently surrendered the shooting rights.

An expert was needed to put all this right. John selected a local farmer whom he held in high regard as having made good from humble beginnings, owning and managing quite a large, very efficient farm. They agreed a partnership on the basis of John providing the majority of the assets and his partner the majority of the management expertise. John had slight initial concern about this selection, due to his new partner's inclination to follow the local hunts to shoot the fox before the hounds got there (there really is nothing new under the sun, is there?). However, John had decided that the modernization of the estate was far more important than the establishment and maintenance of his own personal status amongst the county set.

The matter became even more complicated when his partner suggested that a third partner, however small, would entitle them to form a Socialist Co-operative and the right to apply for a huge grant from the Labour government. This was an irresistible challenge to John, who settled the whole thing by recruiting a Bass accountant to organize and run the finances of the nascent Co-operative. Bass never forgave John for this act of poaching – a little tough, I thought, since they are hardly a scarce resource – but who should care about that, with such an alternative challenge and heritage to occupy you for the rest of your life?

Thus was prepared, in Bass Charrington style and format, what must have been the largest, longest, most comprehensively detailed five-year capital and revenue business plan that the Ministry of Agriculture would ever have seen from a farming enterprise. As a precaution, John had bought himself a new suit (alone, in three minutes, he proudly told me, with his wife in charge of the car on a double yellow line) to perfect the presentation to the Ministry. The net result was a huge grant to set up the Co-operative.

*

One of John's passions was steam trains, not only the narrow-gauge network at the stately home of which he was in total command. He was also heavily involved in railway history, including possession of '*Pendennis Castle*', one of the great railway locomotives of the steam age, and lengths of track on which to run his collection.

Despite the cash-flow problems of the landed gentry, this did not seem to stop John from extravagance to perfect his small-gauge layout. He had selected one of Isambard Kingdom Brunel's famous tunnel facades and had it scaled down, stone by stone, to create an identical miniaturized entrance to his tunnel at Stapleford.

John was often there on summer weekends to drive the visitors around on his trains; indeed, the resident family was always heavily involved in one way or another with the openings of the stately home to the public. The morning after an unusually hot bank holiday, I picked up John from his home to find him in a disconsolate mood: on enquiry about this state of affairs, he told me it was bad enough having an ailing father rushing around looking after visitors, but his mother had fainted while buttering 3000 scones.

Note to file: Learn a lot about life from how available resources are given priority by others.

We all worried about John and his looming inheritance. During a particularly serious management committee meeting at Manchester, where interruptions were only allowed in the case of genuine emergencies, a secretary rushed in to get John out immediately, to take a phone call. We all feared that perhaps this was his impending transfer to becoming His Lordship. Instead, it turned out to be a call from Liverpool Docks to tell him that '*The Flying Scotsman*' had returned from exhibition in the USA, that it could not stand on the dockside after nightfall, and what was John going to do about getting it moved? Our esteem for John rose even higher as he revealed himself to be managing agent for other important collections of magnificent historic railway hardware.

*

Meanwhile, John was adapting himself to life in an ordinary brand new house in an ordinary village, with a baby son and heir, the key that fuelled further his determination to preserve their heritage through the next generation.

At the first sign of serious spring weather, his wife suggested that he might make a start on mowing the lawn. Not being too well possessed with such domestic techniques and technology, he told me that he had borrowed his next-door neighbour's machine and promptly shattered it on the residual builder's rubble hidden in the grass. Consultation on the matter had indicated that he might like to comb the lawn first for such material, which he had set to with a will, to the point of accumulating a number of neat piles of rubble. Enquiring what to do next, and being ordered to dispose of them at the bottom of the garden, he selected the only wheeled transport available to him, namely the baby's pram, the springs of which were unable to sustain the unusual load.

Telling all these weekend tales to a colleague, usually on the following Monday, enabled him perhaps to get the impact of major disasters behind him and out of his system and to switch himself full time to the week's work for Bass; this he carried out with impeccable devotion, to the point that he was to be offered a senior appointment in London, but that is a later story (sorry, disaster).

*

Come summertime, John would get his AC Cobra out of winter wrapping and enjoy this high-speed open-air activity. He enjoyed simply having the car admired in public places; for this purpose he had go-fast stripes the length of the body, dotted intermittently with tiny meaningless coats-of-arms. This raised public interest in the status of the owner in the most modest way possible, but making it perfectly clear that he was not a common enthusiast willing to discuss his hobby with any Tom, Dick or Harry.

Inevitably, I received an invitation to go to Manchester in it. Although it was only the (slightly) lower-powered model, John was well able to demonstrate the necessity, he said, of having to register ownership with the police, being the only vehicle on the road at that time that was uncatchable.

On the way back, it started to rain just before reaching the M6. I suggested that he put the hood up.

"Not necessary, old bean," he shouted as he accelerated into the downpour, "Rain is horizontal at cruising speed."

I have to say that such a journey, on a motorway clear enough of traffic as it was in the early 1970s, needs to be experienced. Once. I spent the next day or two trying to comb the knots out of my hair. Fortunately, John said that Cobra wheel bearings were no longer available and the only affordable options were from Aston Martin, which wore out rather quickly and limited the number of journeys that he could make in any year. Or did he say that as a kindness, to ease my obvious desire to refuse future invitations?

John never opened his heart expecting sympathy or advice, making it very easy for me to listen to him without getting emotionally involved. I could either smile inwardly and make my day, or simply be grateful that it was not happening to me.

Came the day that John told me about the family celebrations on completion of the seven-year handover period of the estate. All was set for the future. Then came notification from the Inland Revenue that the transfer to the Hon John had been invalidated, due to lack of discipline in accounting for the division of labour costs between John's estate and father's house, or some such trivial issue that would pass by any normal human being but should have been picked up by an accountant?

Note to file: Stop being nasty about accountants. They probably can't help it.

John's father was far from giving up at this terrible news, obviously aware of the vital need to carry on for another seven years if the heritage was to last. One thing he did to fill the time was to take a trip to visit his sister in South Africa. This was no ordinary trip, as one might by now expect; not only was apartheid in full swing but she had been spending many years actually living among the native population.

Nor was it ordinary for John, who was instructed to look after the stately home in his father's absence, and presumably to get some practice to boot: and on no account was he to get in touch with father by phone except in the direst emergency. I missed John on the Manchester journey for those few weeks' sojourn at the stately home, but that was more than made up on his return to the real world.

He told me of an evening cuddled up in a small heated room when the front door bell rang, to reveal two policemen asking if they could check the gunroom against the gun licences that His Lordship had. Things like this do not easily faze the likes of such people as John. Expressing total ignorance of his father's affairs, he directed them through the icy hall to the icy gunroom, told them to do what they wanted and returned to the warmth.

Half an hour later they knocked on John's door, entered, informed John that they had found three '303' rifles surplus to the other permitted guns, and could they please have a look round elsewhere. Half an hour later they returned to inform John that they had found thousands of rounds of '303' ammunition, and warned John that his father would be in serious trouble when he returned.

More out of interest in what his father was doing with such weaponry, rather than from the tone of the policemen's threats, John decided that this might still be an occasion to call him up in South Africa, although there was obviously a perfectly good reason for all this. On eventually making contact with father he related the event, but before he could ask *why* he owned the weaponry, his father angrily snapped, 'Thank God they didn't find the rest' and put the phone down.

John promised to satisfy my equal appetite for the answer, when he could get round to extracting it from father. The answer came shortly after father returned. How simple and obvious can one get? At the start of the Second World War in 1939, the family decided that they had all the resources necessary to isolate themselves into total self-sufficiency for the duration of the war, with one exception: meat. How simple to have a few rifles to shoot the deer roaming the woods on the estate.

Nothing more was heard about the affair.

Note to file: What is it that they say about one law for the few, and one for us? Clearly, different needs require different rules.

All good things come to an end. John was offered a director's job in London, which he accepted. When he got there, the job had been downgraded; a man of that integrity and resourcefulness can stand so much until his principles take command. He walked out of Bass after being accused of gutlessness for withdrawing from the challenge he had been given, and went to manage his own affairs. He sold his house in the village: as one might expect, not like anyone else but by sealed tender. He refused the highest bidders because he did not think that the neighbours would like them.

He eventually inherited the title, more than seven years after the previous disaster. This saved the death duties but was not enough to save the stately home. As the new Lord Gretton, he made an enormous contribution to issues in the House of Lords that required analytical skills, but suffered from a fatal illness when far too young.

His son was one of the very last hereditary peers to enrol in the House of Lords, before Blair put an end to all that nonsense.

*

Whilst all the Manchester problems were going on (or off, depending on how one looked at it), there were still four other breweries to look after that deserved equal attention. In the centre of Liverpool, we had a brewery providing an excellent service to the pubs: on occasions more than excellent, judging from mysterious failures to account for all of the beer that had been brewed. Since the sale of the business to Bass, the ex-managing director had been enjoying a contract through to his retirement, coming in most mornings accompanied by dog, Times and Telegraph. Since we had not been told what his function was, we carried on regardless, concluding that he was devoting his time to guarding the company safe in his private office, the contents of which became the subject of some speculative interest.

Because of the relatively happy spirit in the brewery, situated in a large city, it was not surprising to me that the operators belonged to a different trade union from those in Manchester. This union was much more moderate and less organized, due to the membership being widely spread geographically, in small numbers and in a wide variety of jobs. This gave intense pleasure to the personnel director (aka The Snake), who invariably screwed down the official union negotiator to a lesser deal than the other four breweries obtained from their combined annual wage negotiation.

As we came nearer to closure, I became increasingly concerned about the lot of these loyal Liverpool men getting the thick end of the stick, purely because of the less aggressive attitude of their trade union. When the union official accepted a wage settlement offer of £1 per week less than the other union, I could take it no longer and announced that I was not prepared to accept it myself, and told the official that we would award an extra £1 per week to the bonus rate. After all, what was £52 for 30 men, to gain some goodwill during a very sticky run up to closure?

"I'll get you for this," snarled The Snake.

Note to file: If you know that you are going to upset a personnel director, it is better if he is not yours.

Shortly before the closure, the ex-managing director of the brewery retired, and we entertained him in the sample store. In the atmosphere of jollification, we forgot to ask him for the keys of his office and safe until he was halfway down the brewery yard for the last time. Rushing after him, the head brewer received a profuse apology as the precious keys were pressed into his hand. After waiting a respectful time, in other words until he had disappeared beyond the end of the road, a posse was selected to solve the mystery of the contents of the safe, and thus to discover what effect they might have had, and henceforth would have on our running of the operation.

The initial anticlimax (often defined as that feeling when you lift a fig leaf and find a fig) of finding the safe packed full of old company ties, was soon replaced by intense guilt when it was discovered that they were, in fact, icons of a long family tradition. All employees, to the most lowly, used to be invited to the boardroom on the day of their 13th anniversary of joining the company, to receive a valedictory address from the chairman and directors, with the ceremonial handing over of a company tie as a personal gift, in recognition of faithful long service. If only we had known, we could have kept up a whole series of inspirational morale-boosting parties.

*

Note to file: Always explore the wisdom of elders, no matter how bizarre or potentially unfruitful the prospect. You will always find a pearl.

Over in Blackpool, we had a lovely little brewery, full of respectful operators with views somewhat at variance from their union colleagues in Manchester, from where their union discipline officially emanated. The brewers had mastered the control of any mutterings of centrally enforced strike action, because the shop steward and other union activists all owned seaside boarding houses, and made more money from them than they earned in the brewery.

They were ordered not to be so unbrotherly as to deprive their fellow members from earning a living by going on strike, whilst they retained their own lucrative activities. This proved to be such powerful logic that they readily agreed.

Only once did the annual joint wage negotiations for the four breweries reach stalemate, when a three-line-whip one-day strike was ordered, giving seven days notice to the company. On the due day, the head brewer came in to find all the operators present and correct. Having made all the preparations not to brew that day, he found himself in somewhat of a quandary; he could hardly ask the men what on earth they thought they were doing coming into work, so he wisely decided to act dim and simply get everyone to start brewing, and wait to see what happened.

Late that afternoon, the shop steward knocked on the door of the head brewer's office, entered, and started off, "Excuse me, sir....." Could this have been the last time that a shop steward ever called a manager 'sir'? He then apologized profusely for forgetting that the men ought to have been on strike that day, and in view of this, would it be convenient if they went on strike tomorrow instead?

Coping with surrealism was not in my management handbook, so I decided to avoid excessive management involvement in this (so far) harmless domestic variant from operational norms. But this rather cowardly use of discretion was to be sorely tested, and very soon.

The following week, I arrived at the brewery to see painted, in 4-ft high letters along the brewery wall, 'STOP RITUAL KILLING HERE'. Somewhat punch-drunk at the time, because of the goings on at the Manchester brewery, I could feel nothing but dread of some awful disaster organized by the forces of evil somewhere out there in Blackpool.

It was with some relief that eventually it turned out to be just a case of mistaken identity, with an abattoir down the road suspected by an animal rights group of illicit ethnic slaughterhouse practices.

Quite soon after, a beer quality failure occurred, only identified in the pubs and reported late on Christmas Eve, so the beer could not be exchanged until after the peak Christmas drinking sessions. This type of occurrence, at the busiest times, is generally considered to be the ultimate cardinal sin that a brewer can commit.

Although the reason was quickly identified, and the situation brought back to normal, the event may have proved too stressful for the brewer involved. He suddenly announced that, despite his long and loyal service to the company, he could no longer offer his services at the brewery between sunset on Fridays and sunset on Saturdays.

When he declared that this was purely personal, with neither religious nor other extra-terrestrial motive, the only thing that I could do was to process this impossible situation through the best counselling that the company could offer. With thanks to the skill of The Snake, we were able to wave him goodbye with feelings of justice having been done, in the knowledge that, from then on, he could happily pursue his new-found (but still unrevealed) interest *every* day of the week.

Neither did the local sales manager seem to have recovered completely from the shock of the duff Christmas beer. He became convinced that it was an evil spell cast over the brewery that would cost him bonus-earning sales every Christmas from then on: this was despite our protestations to reassure him that no factors whatsoever, either worldly or astrological, could conceivably cause a repetition. However he did seem slightly relieved when I told him that next Christmas the moon would be in a different phase.

*

Note to file: Things can quite suddenly turn surreal, with no warning. When they do, be prepared for a wave of totally unpredictable bizarre events.

My favourite breweries had to be in Burnley, and its satellite in Barrow-in-Furness. The latter was manned by a foreman and four operators only, all of them being the kind of salt-of-the-earth characters that one finds in places that are relatively remote geographically from the hub of things. In these circumstances, they usually have an especially strong tendency towards self-sufficiency and contentment.

The brewery was tiny, and sales were such that the premium cask beer only needed to be brewed once a month; not that the customers seemed to mind when it got a bit old, they simply turned to the standard bitter. The technical brewing book consisted of a girlie calendar on the wall of the office, on which the brewings were written above the appropriate dates, as and when telephoned from the head brewer in Burnley. His occasional visits to the brewery were sufficient to keep this lovely little operation going with no difficulty whatsoever, without, of course, the remotest trade union influence.

As the inevitable closure approached, the men were told of their severance payments, at which they asked me how they would be paid. Replying that the normal procedure was to hand them their cheques on the last day, they immediately went into a huddle. The foreman then broke away, and spoke on behalf of all of them.

"I'm sorry, but we're not much into cheques in these parts. We would take less if you made it cash."

Thirty years on, I still often wonder exactly what it is in our modern society that justified us throwing such contentment and way of life into the waste bin of obsolescence.

*

Note to file: Be careful how much you support so-called 'progress'. It may be at the expense of a social structure that is of greater value than that of your strategic goal.

The Burnley brewery employees had similar characteristics, in the sense of great loyalty engendered by the close involvement of the previous board of directors in the day-to-day running of the brewery. Although union members, the operators would either studiously ignore any instructions from Manchester to take industrial action, or, in hypercritical situations, earnestly discuss the issue at stake until it was too late to obey the action ordered.

Despite, or perhaps because of this, it was to prove to be one of the most difficult closures to handle. For a start, the brewery was a core feature of the town's social life; the company owned virtually all the pubs in the town, and by far and away the most popular beer was the 'Burnley Bitter'. On top of this, the delays in the construction of the new brewery at Runcorn required the 'Burnley Bitter' to be removed from the pubs and replaced with the new regional brand well before the closure.

Clearly, resistance was going to come as much from the customers as from the brewery itself, as and when the town's name disappeared from its favourite tipple. We already had plenty of experience of fanatical peculiarities in drinking habits exclusive to the Burnley folk.

There was then (and possibly still is) as much Benedictine liqueur drunk in Burnley as in the whole of the rest of the country, often taken as a 'Benny Hot' - Benedictine in hot water - as a chaser to their pint of beer. This habit had arisen from the town's regimental involvement with the Benedictine distillery in Northern France, during both world wars. The degree of involvement had clearly been way beyond the call of military duty, and had thus become fully integrated into the town's heritage.

In addition, I distinctly recall, even after 30 years, being given only sterilized milk in the coffee offered during my visits. This was before the extensive introduction of today's UHT palatable imitation of fresh milk; in those days it came in thick glass bottles with a crown cork on the neck, exactly like a clear glass beer bottle, but with a foul off-white liquid inside, tasting of burnt, watered down condensed milk.

It was eventually explained to me that this Burnley phenomenon of drinking sterilized milk was due to an outbreak of tuberculosis or brucellosis from infected milk in the 1920s, 50 years before.

The change of their favourite beer to a generic, widely advertised brand name was clearly going to require immense tact and anticipation, to pre-empt the ultra-conservative reaction expected.

Note to file: Always include local history in the equation of your business tactics. You will never forecast accurately any reaction, but afterwards you will be able to prove that you did your best. But expect your boss to remark 'Pity it wasn't good enough'.

No-one could ever have come near to anticipating what happened in this particular case. We left the changeover of the beer to the very end, after the rest of the TV region had been converted to the new brand, and wide TV advertising started. A build-up of local confidence in the product was conducted, with organised tastings and local publicity for the launch.

A decision was then taken to select one weekend for converting every single pub, club, hotel and sundry licensed establishment, when all the old beer in the cellars would be removed, at the same time replacing all the 'Burnley Bitter' counter mounts and displays in the bars. Self-congratulation was the order of the day, for a mammoth exercise brilliantly organized and achieved.

The stunning reward for this manifested itself through half the labour force of the town going down with the trots, judging from the demand on the doctors' surgeries on the Monday morning. Some doctors quickly assumed the source, in some cases even signing the sick notes as 'brewtenitis' (the new beer was called Brew Ten).

This phenomenon was completely unexpected, since similar past experiences had applied only to introductions of classic Burton ales brewed with the high-sulphate water from the historic wells (a dose of salts in every glass). Even with that type of beer, only relatively small numbers of new consumers require a modicum of acclimatization, (reputedly best relieved, by popular acclaim, through temporary accommodation of the toilet roll in the fridge).

Note to file: Crises, when remote from immediate help, require balanced judgment, decisiveness, not a little psychology, and the ability to filter back the right information to your distant superiors on a need-to-know basis. This will invariably be analyzed with the benefit of both factlessness and hindsight, so expect all your decisions to prove to have been totally wrong.

On this occasion, I opted for a brief report to the centre involving the circumstances, of everything under control, and nothing worse than a case of temporary mass hysteria at the disappearance of a piece of the town's heritage. This evoked a curt telephone message discarding such a ludicrous assumption, and that, with effect from 10.30 am. the next morning, Dr Rainbow would take personal command of this serious medical threat.

Being uncertain of the requirements of this most highly regarded boffin-cum-human-being, I ordered the brewery to have available all manner of sterilized swabs and sampling equipment to await his arrival. Stepping from his chauffeur-driven car, Cyril warmly renewed old acquaintances and made his announcement.

"Right, as you know, I've been sent up here to find out to what degree the new beer is dishing out Montezuma's Revenge. There's only one way to find out. When do the pubs open?"

There ensued a technical evaluation under trade conditions. Uninformed readers should not immediately think that this is just another term for a pub crawl; there are, in fact, differences, but which escape me for the moment. The evaluation was on a scale to allow the entry into Cyril's bodily systems of a quantity of the beer sufficient to produce, in Cyril's own judgment, a statistically significant result. Fortunately, the town's licences at that time allowed pub closure at 3 pm. (as against 2 pm. elsewhere in the country), thus allowing a generous over-measure of fluid intake as well as a slap-up lunch to help things along. Finally, levered back into his car, he was able to wind down the window and call out, as he was swept away, "I'll report back tomorrow!"

The inevitable result was 'no effect': inevitable because there had to be some doubt about the statistical validity of the venerable doctor's gastrointestinal functions, which had been hardened by decades of favouritism towards the classic of all classic Burton beers, Worthington White Shield. In fact, his colleagues were often confused as to why he spent so much of his time researching into this one brand, which required such a regular replenishment of the pile of crates in the corner of his laboratory.

Note to file: There can be many reasons for unusually high demand for 'consumable stores' in a research department. But it will usually be well targeted and give beneficial results.

There is a maxim, which is reasonably specific to the brewing industry, saying 'almost any news about its products is good news'. This is because it invariably elicits intense interest, debate and resultant thirst amongst serious beer drinkers. As is well known, the press has never been slow to oblige on this subject, being so near to the hearts of *its* serious consumers. However, this particular event in Burnley, potentially the great beer story of the year, was missed by the tabloids. This was partly because the medical problem disappeared as fast as it had arisen, and partly because they had received a tip-off that the new brand of beer being advertised was different either side of the Pennines.

The brighter journalists had worked out that there must be a boundary somewhere near Burnley, where deliveries from Yorkshire and Lancashire meet; they found this, running down the centre of a street with our pubs on either side. Weeks of excitement were generated with 'spot the beer', and 'how much of each can you drink?' competitions, all of which gave a tremendous boost to the TV launch across the region.

Such 'regionalization' of beer flavours within the same brand name was, in fact, quite common at that time, since by far and away the most important geography of branding lay in the commercial TV regions, for economy in advertising. Several brewing companies actually made these local variations in flavour a big selling point. In our particular case, we were bowing to the distinctive requirements of our customers either side of the Pennines; more bitter and drier than average to the east, less bitter and slightly sweeter to the west.

The debate was so popular that one tabloid, which had been a bit slow off the mark, tried to grab the limelight by claiming that there was *no* difference between Bass and Worthington beers! They cited Draught Bass and Worthington E; Bass Blue Triangle and Worthington Green Shield; Bass Red Triangle and Worthington White Shield: in fact, pairing up most of the great historic Burton beers from the one stable. Unaware of the fanatical following that existed for one brand or the other among beer drinkers, the newspaper's proposition outraged so many of its readers that the subject disappeared from the scene as fast as had the Burnley Runs.

Thirty years on, with none of those beer twins now in existence, there lies a great opportunity for beer historians to research, and debate eternally, what must be one of the most interesting beer mysteries of all time: what *were* the differences between Bass and Worthington beers?

It is, in fact, outstandingly difficult to be precise about the detail of the flavour of any particular beer. The technique of quantifying beer flavour circles round the relative flavour intensity of certain known chemical compounds present in all beers. This is rather unlike wine, where the experts seem to have the opportunity to exploit an infinity of terms, ranging from the most exotic fruits (other than grapes), through familiar household aromas, to kangaroo's armpits. Personally I prefer my wine to taste of wine.

Nevertheless, brewers avoid at their peril the existence of a small number of 'experts' among any group of eight pints-a-night beer drinkers: there were plenty of those in the 1970s. I do not refer to the inevitable barrack-room lawyers shouting out their prejudices, nor to the quiet followers who would like to be considered as part of the cognoscenti, but to the real appreciators of subtle differences in beer flavours.

They may not be able to describe them technically, but can identify them well enough to help a brewery keep track of the likes and dislikes of these dedicated groups of opinion formers. This was the case (we thought) when a small chain of high-consumption working men's clubs in Yorkshire refused to purchase the new beer brand. In deference to the profitability of keeping the trade, of which there was enough to justify brewing a special beer for them, it was agreed to go on supplying their old brand.

However, beer tastes changed in the course of a year or two, as lager was becoming a popular alternative to draught bitter. This resulted in sales of the latter declining, to the point of quality problems with maintaining the supply of the special beer to those particular clubs. It fell on the shoulders of the sales director to talk one of the clubs into secretly taking one week's delivery of the new brand and to sell it through the old beer taps, to assess the true degree of resistance. Returning to the club a week later, the steward reported to him:

"No problems whatsoever. Unfortunately, I accidentally put your beer on the Whitbread pumps, and theirs on yours, and they still didn't notice any difference!"

Note to file: Never be discouraged by a customer reaction that you would have preferred not to have heard. You can always explain it away as the exception that proves the rule - once.

This stunning blow to one's pride marked the end of my stint in the north, with the temptation from the company to return to the source of all wisdom. But, after only three years, Burton was never to be the same again.

CHAPTER 7

AN UNDOER'S ROLE IN MANAGEMENT

Approaching the mid-1970s, the whole country was awash with industrial unrest, and inflation was beginning to take off from both a trebling of the oil price and, some claimed, from the effect of decimalization in 1971. The brewery merger madness had quietened down, although the new era of outsiders moving in on the big pub owners – Grand Metropolitan Hotels and Imperial Tobacco – were becoming a different kind of threat to the future of pubs. Alternative uses of pubs other than as beer outlets were clearly on the cards, as was the future existence of small 'locals' if the vertical integration in the industry came under threat (discussed in Chapter 10).

In Burton, the private trains and 30 railway crossings had gone, and Bass had concentrated its brewing on only one site, albeit with main streets still running through it, and producing as much beer as ever. A concentration of distribution into road transport was taking place as a result of the popularity of keg beer, the use of light weight aluminium casks for cask beer, and the failure of British Rail to be able to offer a slick, efficient container freight service to meet the needs of the day. The combined union effect at Runcorn and British Rail was not a good start for this brand new brewery, and which dogged its efficiency for the years to come.

Burton was being honoured by the arrival of the whole Bass Charrington ivory tower HQ administration, as well as the complete central marketing operation, from their snug existence in central London. The willingness of the majority of these undoers to transfer so far north to Staffordshire must have owed much to the designer of the 'delights of Burton upon Trent' brochure handed out to everyone invited to move there. It must have been the inspiration of a genius, to argue successfully against the alternative of generous redundancy and a continuing existence in the smoke.

An era had passed, but another was clearly starting, with all kinds of new people to come to terms with and, of course, so many exciting new things to learn.

*

Since my new job in 1973 was the provision of a technical research service to all our breweries countrywide, as well as to the marketing HQ's product development department, I regrettably had to admit to having come within the classification of undoer; but this had the great advantage of qualifying for the senior executives' dining facilities, and thus the opportunity to muck in with the ivory tower lot.

It was surprising how many in the ivory tower qualified for senior executive status; so, although work was banned as a discussion subject over lunch, it did not prevent the creation of an understanding of the behind-the-scenes workings of a huge group, and quickly the discovery of their contempt for the doers. It soon became obvious to me that the ivory tower saw the complexities of business starting with cheap product at the factory gate, after which the undoers take over to create its success.

One must try to understand this contempt for the contribution of production people, because it is universal in British industry and rare in other countries strong in manufacturing. The origin of this attitude is obscure, but it is credible to speculate that production specialists are feared because they have to do things that only they themselves fully understand, and this is best compensated for by treating them as lesser beings.

With this in mind, all credit had to go to the marketing chief, whose main experience in life had been amongst the bizarre world of advertising agents in London, when he invited himself to meet some brewers on their own ground; or, as he put it, 'I really must go and visit the factory. I have never set foot in one before'. He came from that world of ignorance of how to travel by tube or bus; of Gucci, Annabel's and monogrammed shirts; of social connections (both real and imaginary) to separate him from all the rest. Combined with the wherewithal to maintain the standards and status that he knew he justly deserved, this made him just the sort of person to mix in well with Staffordshire folk.

He arrived at the sample store in his long dark trench coat, black Homburg, and small dark purple spectacles capable of concealing all manner of personal hang-ups about mixing with the plebs. His pallid face necessarily reflected more an active club life in a big city than exposure to fresh air and sunshine in a rural environment. Welcomed by the (agog) head brewer, he was introduced to the brewery staff as the man responsible for the presentation of our famous brands to the public, and with a polite enquiry whether he would like to enjoy a Draught Bass or one of the full ranges of excellent keg beers that he advertised. His reply was to the consternation of all.

"Don't try that sort of stuff on me," he announced, "I'll have a gin and tonic."

Thus an important figure, for the first time ever, found himself firmly ejected from the hospitality of the brewery sample store. His similarity to a certain television character in a certain comedy series of German occupation of France in the Second World War, was not recognised for some years. In fact, it was only after the company car policy first allowed foreign cars onto the approved list, when he chose a black Mercedes, that he forever earned himself the nickname of Herr Flick.

Note to file: Restraint in difficult circumstances is a great virtue.

My first major project was to organize and run a technical conference, for the whole of the new group now centred on Burton. A chain of hotels had been purchased from Esso, more or less the prototype of the modern middle grade business motel, of reasonable but standardized accommodation with conference facilities. It was only natural to select the nearest of these for this groundbreaking event.

I designed a programme that would involve interaction between the ivory tower and brewery staff from across the country. It would also allow debate and understanding of each other's objectives, and help to coalesce relationships now that we were effectively neighbours. I took my proposed conference programme to the production company managing director for approval.

"Don't bother me with that, I'm sure it's fine," he said, "but there is only one thing you must get right.The Colonel [our chairman] will be coming to the dinner on the last night, and you must make absolutely sure that the port is served correctly."

Note to file: Always be aware of the diversity of priorities amongst your seniors, and be prepared to honour them.

The following day I hurried to the hotel to discuss this minor detail, only to discover that the hotel held no stock of port, either there or centrally.

"OK," I said to the manager, "I'll get a suitable port for the chairman from company stocks, and you just provide the glasses."

"We don't have any port glasses," he replied.

"Get some, and decanters too. They will hold you in good stead for the future," I suggested, "meanwhile let's talk about your procedure for serving it."

This was a stupid suggestion really, considering that obviously he had never done it, let alone seen it done. As the time for the conference approached, the best waitress in the hotel was selected to serve the chairman's table, and was duly taught the art and mystery of serving port. A special red blob would be put on the chairman's place card to identify him, and all she had to do was to put the decanter on his right hand side, at the right time, and then withdraw. We would do everything else.

Following a highly successful conference, even the dinner started to go well, until the time for port. The chosen waitress had been taken ill suddenly, and although the substitute had correctly identified the red blob and the right hand side of the chairman, she then interrupted his conversation, directly into his ear, with "Like some port, duck?"

*

Note to file: In my book, Sod's Law is 'If anything can go wrong, it will', and Murphy's Law is 'If nothing can go wrong, it still will'. But, in most cases, it doesn't really seem to matter which is which.

As always, the brewery and other technical operations continued to maintain an effort to control costs as a matter of good management practice, however much the extravagances of the neighbouring ivory tower might have seemed. Even Arthur, who was still in charge of the Burton brewery, had noted the increasing piles of paper, and had a survey done which concluded that two administrative photocopies were being printed for every barrel of beer produced. This may seem trivial expenditure, until one considers that the brewery was turning out well over one million barrels of beer per year.

This was the era of rapid development of administration technology, when photocopiers had only recently moved from wet copying on special paper to modern fast printing on to ordinary stationery. This yielded enormous opportunities for those who felt that their careers would benefit from distributing the results of their labours to all and sundry. The larger machines were considered luxury complex items in those days, therefore sited centrally and operated by trained staff; in our case we shared the ivory tower's.

There was nothing Arthur liked more than a challenge, particularly when he could measure the results in simple figures. He set about a major efficiency drive to reduce consumption of paper from two to one photocopy per barrel of beer produced, and achieved it within a matter of months. Two days after the announcement of the achievement (and appropriate celebration lubricated by the brewery stock of Worthington White Shield), a memo came round from the ivory tower telling everyone that a new photocopying machine had just been installed, capable of a zillion copies per hour collatable into an infinite variety of volumes of hundreds of pages, and could they please have some orders in order to justify the capital expenditure.

*

Note to file: It is important to learn and adapt to a company's procedures for justifying capital expenditure.

One of the joys of working in an industry like brewing is the opportunity to get out and see your raw materials in the fields round about harvest time. Farmers and barley merchants were delighted to see the brewers, and invariably the most senior brewing directors would use these opportunities to meet their less senior staff during these hospitable visits, as each got their turn to be invited on these annual jaunts. When you are buying 100,000 tons of barley each year, you tend to be quite well received by the suppliers.

In between wading through fields of best malting barley in the nicest parts of eastern England, taking sample handfuls and assessing their quality under the guidance of the most senior maltsters, the opportunity was taken to discuss current brewing issues. Before one particular trip, the hottest talk was of the brewers in Burton having recently joined a trade union; this was unheard of, and in Burton too, the ultimate home of paternalism! Also in Burton at that time there was a temporary technical problem with the Burton Union sets used for fermenting the traditional Burton ales, caused by unusually high summer temperatures.

The managing director opened a discussion by asking Norman, one of the Burton brewers, the state of the union problem in the Burton brewery.

"It's all higher management's fault......" he started off, presumably aware that he was addressing the highest of higher management itself, thus leaving the MD to puzzle about his own role in such a minor technical problem.

After Norman had elucidated the frustrations of the brewers' feelings of isolation from any company communication system or career development plan, the MD finally twigged that Norman was referring to the *Trade* Union, not the *Burton* union problem. Known generally as the Smiling Hatchet Man, the MD smiled and appeared very grateful to have been kept informed of current attitudes amongst his junior staff. Thirty years later, Norman completed a most distinguished career in North America.

Note to file: Always have some options available when you have the courage to speak your mind to your masters.

This confusion of the meaning of 'unions' in Burton had other entertaining high spots. It was the era of Japan taking intense interest in foreign industrial practices, and we had many visits from camera-laden Japanese brewers, who were particularly impressed by our century-old equipment and brewing techniques. On one occasion of cameras flashing at the hundreds of large wooden barrels assembled into a whole array of Burton union sets in one huge room, one of the visitors enquired, in very broken English, something about the state of union conditions in the brewery.

"Oh," replied the brewery guide, "to ensure the best conditions, we take their heads off once a year, give them a good scrubbing out and then put them back."

Loud acclaims of "Ah so," accompanied by unanimous nods of full comprehension and satisfaction, clearly left the visitors fully briefed on our industrial relations practices.

*

For some considerable time, pressure had been slowly building up on the British brewing industry from an organisation called the Campaign for Real Ale (CAMRA), as more and more breweries converted a significant amount of their draught beer production from cask to keg beer. This had been particularly prevalent in London and the south east, and, as we all know, if something happens there that causes a stir, it automatically extrapolates to national importance.

The case being made by the group was that the traditional clarification and maturation of flavour of cask beer in the pub cellar (so-called real ale) were being replaced by grossly inferior fizzy products, 'sanitized' and standardized in the brewery. The case made by the breweries was that the time had come to meet customers' aspirations for consistent brighter beer in the glass, free from both flavour and gas variations, and the risk of unpleasant bits floating in the beer, these being the inevitable consequence of cask beer quality being in the hands of tens of thousands of publicans. Also, those publicans who did have the pride, experience and reputation for serving excellent cask beer were becoming increasingly scarce, as pressure came upon newcomers to develop more general management skills in the running of pubs.

It was inevitable that this modernization would take place, but there was no reason for cask beers to disappear altogether, so long as there were enough cognoscenti left to appreciate the vagaries of such products. 'Let them have their fish guts and seaweed in their beer, if that's how they want it,' was the cry of the manufacturers of the cask beer clarifying agents (derived universally from those savoury sources).

The early conversion away from cask beer was more significant among the big London brewers (apart from Bass Charrington, for ever the largest cask beer producers), and it was happening at a time of some other rather unfortunate incidents. Firstly, the great accumulation of brewing empires in the previous decade or so had resulted in a near monopoly for Watney Mann (recently taken over by Grand Metropolitan Hotels) in parts of East Anglia. They had used this to start a closure programme of unprofitable village pubs: this was the first sign of a major brewer showing a greater interest in maximizing profitability at the expense of customer service – the small cloud on the horizon that developed into the storm 20 years later which destroyed the industry's culture and heritage.

At the same time a new keg beer called Watney's Red was being introduced, heavily advertised with Russian connotations when relations between Britain and Russia were not exactly chummy. This unfortunate mistake came to be compared with a similar disaster that Schlitz suffered in the United States with a new type of beer: in that instance the name of their company also did not exactly help their cause.

Note to file: Do not underestimate the power of the consumer to be able to reject a new product purely because of its name.

Also at that time keg lager, a beer not suitable in cask form, was just beginning to be recognized as a serious competitor to traditional British beers. What better combination of factors could there have been to expand a consumer group's interest in preserving an archaic tradition, into a campaign for preserving the village pub, condemning keg ales as unpalatable and unwanted, and fighting off the 'threat' of 'European' beer. The degree to which CAMRA became successful in these objectives, and its involvement in the implosive collapse of the British brewing industry at the turn of the millennium, will develop in future chapters.

To return to the real world of the mid-1970s, and the effect of the general trades unions' recalcitrance of the day, the major decision had been taken to abandon British Rail and distribute all our centrally produced beers around the country by road, requiring a large fleet of trunkers based largely in Burton. By a great flash of brilliance, a retired brigadier (who had trained under General Montgomery during the war as organiser of logistics) was appointed to set up the whole of this trunking operation from scratch.

Thus was born one of the most respected fleets in the country, in terms of quality of appearance, maintenance and efficiency. It seemed only a matter of months before a formal invitation arrived to attend the official opening. We were seated on a temporary grandstand, briefed by the brigadier on the role of the trunking operation, then he introduced the new manager of the operation, a certain Major James.

Major James described the separate functions before inviting us to split up into small parties and inspect the whole site. I chose to go round with the manager himself, who, during the tour of the garage facilities, managed to introduce us to a warrant officer supervisor, a sergeant foreman, a corporal charge-hand, and a lance-corporal shop steward.

Note to file: There are many ways of creating a favourable, disciplined environment in the workplace.

By 1975 this operation was working so well that the brigadier could comfortably retire off the scene, but such was his enthusiasm for the company, and theirs for him, that he was invited to command the setting up of the Bass Museum of Brewing History. This was due to be opened in 1977 to mark the bicentenary of Bass.

This project was a different kettle of fish altogether. It

involved a concept never before tackled by the company, namely that of presenting a national heritage to the public, on the brewery site, on a limited budget, largely with volunteer help, yet to a standard that the company and the whole town would be proud of.

Clearly the brigadier was the ideal choice, although he inevitably slightly misinterpreted the objective. For a man who had specialized in the logistics of moving whole armies across foreign territory largely by scrounging local resources, with little time to be confused by too many facts in his urgency to achieve performance and excellence, the project would definitely have to be on a somewhat different scale than that envisaged by the company. Nothing less than a critical mass and a national image was required, that would necessitate continuous development and improvement of the museum thereafter.

There was little interference from on high during the two years of getting the museum established; he was given a capital allocation of £40,000 to spend, and told just to get on with it. Which he did, at least to the point when the ivory tower accountants noticed a discrepancy of £400,000 in their *revenue* accounts attributable to museum development. He was a man after my own heart - surely money comes in only one colour, and whether it is capital or revenue expenditure is nothing more nor less than a taxation issue, which keeps accountants usefully employed in managing such trivial matters. The fact that it needed an extra 0 for anyone to notice what was going on, and in the wrong ledger to boot, must have meant something, I thought.

I got some sort of an answer two years later. The finance director organized a tour of the museum for his daughter's school class, and when presented with the refreshment bill by the museum, he tried to get all the company parents (of those who had a daughter in that class) to share the cost of the food provided.

"What's the total amount involved?" I asked, in response to his phone call.

131

"£18," was his reply.

"Surely to God you can lose that in your accounts somewhere?" I posited, wondering at the same time if the poor man was grossly underpaid.

"I probably could if it was 18 *thousand,*" he replied. Q.E.D.

*

Note to file: Look after the pennies and the pounds will look after themselves. Or something like that.

The mid 1970s were also years of increasing political influence on industry. Left wing legislation on industrial relations practices was putting more and more power into the hands of the trades unions. It was not necessarily a bad thing to get bad employers to behave in a responsible way towards the expectations of their workers to share in the growing wealth of the economy. Unfortunately, as always, it is these employers who take as little notice as possible of such matters, leaving the good profitable companies to be answerable to the public, and thus to be taken to the cleaners by militants' demands.

It is quite horrifying to read, in the new millennium, some historians claiming that the failure to join Europe with full vigour right from the start was a far more important factor in the post-war weakness of British industry than 'badly managed' industrial relations. Authors quote relatively low levels of days lost through strikes, oblivious to the restrictive practices strangling companies, accumulated through years of union power. These practices were strengthening their hold further as the financial institutions (the City) were starting to demand short-term performance and expressing intolerance towards costly disputes. Thus it was far easier, indeed expedient, to give in to a strike threat than to risk the wrath of the providers of your capital, and their 'guardians' in the City, just as it was proving more difficult to invest capital that was offering anything other than a short-term return.

This union grip on big successful organizations had no national boundaries. In 1976, flying to Melbourne to give a scientific paper at a brewing convention, I found myself sitting next to an Australian production manager, to whom I aired my concerns about the future of British industry under the influence of such widespread organized trouble-making. I also enquired whether I could pick up some useful advice on good labour relations Australian style.

"Whatever you do in Australia," he responded, "don't mention a word about industrial relations. The whole of my country is coming under the influence of militant immigrants, mostly from Wales [!], and we see ourselves rapidly getting into the same position as you. And it's seen as being entirely your fault!"

At least I was able to admire a highly efficient, straightforward beer business in Australia: beer was supplied into refrigerated cellars, delivered through refrigerated pipes into refrigerated glasses. In view of the enormous rate of consumption, I thought that the glasses were surprisingly small, until it was explained that quick consumption stopped the beer from warming up. This did nothing to reduce the effect of the 6 o'clock swill, for which Australia had been infamous for many years.

In attempts to overcome this infamy, we in the UK have to be enormously grateful to the Australians for their discovery that the best way of drastically reducing drunkenness at closing time was to *relax* restrictions on licensing hours, albeit in the face of continuous resistance by temperance movements that one sees throughout the world. Our own licensing hours are now, finally, becoming the triumph of common sense over such dogma.

In terms of beer style, however, it is difficult to see how these Australian beers eventually became recognized as so desirable by the British drinker. Advertised in the UK as Australian coast-to-coast nationwide brands, when they were actually no more than leading or second brands in one or two states at best, must be a significant part of marketing's (and the gullible public's) contribution to the implosion of the traditional British brewing industry.

I also had the chance to visit New Zealand, where they were still measuring land in perches (as in rods, poles and...), but I found an amazingly advanced technology for take-home beer. If you had a towbar on your car, you could drive into the brewery on a Saturday to pick up a refrigerated 180-gallon tank of beer on a trailer, fitted with all the necessary dispense equipment for your weekend barbecue.

Note to file: Broadening your knowledge of others' ways of life helps you to become more certain of your own.

Returning to the gloom hanging over British industry, the brewery at Runcorn had been open for a year or two, and to an outsider (which seemed the best thing to be at the time) it gave a fair impression of being run by a committee of shop stewards. This was probably not strictly so, but the whole group had experienced their instant demands to take the lion's share of employee representation on beneficial issues such as the pension fund, as well as their major efforts to try to break the local negotiation rights of each of the other dozen or so of our major breweries scattered around the cities of the United Kingdom.

It is something to be said for the loyalty and pride of their fellow employees in the other Bass breweries that in no way were they going to be deprived of their rights to control their own local dealings with the company. They were clearly not in favour of whatever advantages might exist in one central trade union negotiating body, led by militants. Burton was the obvious prime brewery target to try to crack first, but attempts to gain access through the brewery gates were repelled by their own 'comrades'.

In the Runcorn brewery itself, any type of informal social relationship between 'management' and 'workers' was forbidden by the shop steward committee, clearly indicating an intentional conflict between 'them and us', and to retain that status in as powerful a form as possible. This could only be explained as political at worst, or cultural at best.

Such was this state of industrial relations that, when it was time to do some career shuffles, it was decided to despatch Arthur from Burton to run the Runcorn brewery, and to practise his bonhomie and social skills on attaining a semblance of co-operation and pleasure in the field of human relations. The fact that he failed miserably to break through this impermeable barrier (a sadness as much to him as the company) did not mar appreciation of his ability to keep things running, and for him to earn the ultimate honour from our local trading company of having a pub named after him - The Jolly Brewer.

With Arthur's departure for Runcorn, I was invited to take over the running of the Burton Brewery, and thus return to my natural habitat of a doer.

CHAPTER 8

COPING WITH EXTERNAL INFLUENCES

The mid-1970s involved juggling with a variety of problems and opportunities. Political interference was escalating, blaming businesses for the continuing inflation over which the government had found no sensible national solution. Meanwhile, companies were making little headway with industrial relations, in the face of continued trades union influence and power. No-one seemed to be relating the two.

Lager was still a minor proportion of beer sales, but interest was increasing and all the major brewers were lining themselves up, mostly with imported brands. Bass was far better placed than most, in that Carling lager had already become effectively a 'home' brand, despite its North American heritage. The Canadian owners sensibly seemed more than happy to allow the brand to find its own flavour and character that best suited the British market, so long as consistency with the international reputation of the brand (and presumably ensuing royalties) was maintained.

With the inclusion of the well-known Tennent's Lager international brand, brewed in Scotland within the group's portfolio of beers, Bass was well set to exploit these developments in the preferences of British beer drinkers.

This move by the beer-drinking public towards lager styles was attributed at that time, by most marketeers, to the increasing tendency to taking holidays abroad, thereby experiencing good alternatives to the warm, flat cask beer unique to Britain. This attribution was never proved as valid, but it certainly influenced a general panic to acquire continental and international brands into British beer portfolios. In the meantime, Bass was identified by CAMRA as a special evil, in producing its own increasingly successful lagers at the expense of traditional ales, conveniently ignoring (for the next 25 years) that Bass remained by far and away the largest producer of the largest number of local and national cask beer brands in the world.

*

The diversity of responsibilities and duties of running a whole operation came home smartly and quickly. In my very first week the security manager requested an urgent appointment; I had never met him, but his force of security officers had provided a surveillance service to my previous HQ research department. However, being employed in the brewery, his only formal contact with the HQ 'undoers' that he serviced was through the brewery hierarchy.

I knew that he was ex-RAF regiment, therefore a man of well trained integrity, discipline and loyalty, and I was looking forward to reconciling this certain knowledge with his reputation that I had heard spoken of, that if Hitler had won the war he would be running Staffordshire.

I was greeted by a strong but most affable and respectful personality (perhaps Hitler was like that too, in the right circumstances), in the face of obvious frustration.

"I have been having problems with HQ staff for ages, which your predecessor in command of this brewery didn't seem to be able to do much about," he started at me. "If I can't get them to discipline themselves properly in the interests of all of us, then I can't exert my influence properly on orderly conduct in the brewery. You must help me before the situation becomes critical."

"Sounds serious," I observed, "what's the *specific* problem?"

"The buggers won't park their cars where they ought to. The worst is the research department, leaving their cars all around the 'no parking' zones, interrupting the flow of the delivery fleet."

I have always believed that God invented and gave us time for one reason only, namely to make sure that everything can't happen all at once. However, at that instant I felt that I went through a complete cycle of manic depression, consisting of a terrible low, because it was *me* he had been complaining about, with a high that the security of the brewery (even with main roads running through it) must be in excellent order if that was all he was worried about. Or was he trying to get his own back on my successor in research, who had been promoted from the brewery lab?

It was from there that he had infuriated the security officers by gluing electric plugs into their sockets, to prevent the night security patrol's habit of removing non-essential connections to the power station. Or was it paranoia in me to be thinking that this might be subtle blackmail to line me up with his own personal ambitions, as yet unidentified?

"David", I said, as quickly, encouragingly and authoritatively as possible under the circumstances, "I promise you that I will do something about it." It took, I suppose, about four months to work out how to come to terms with my reluctance to change my spots, aided, I must say, by steadily increasing pressure from our David. Finally, there was no other option than to take the bull by the horns, and I went into print.

'Dear Tony', I started my note to the new head of research, 'It may not be obvious to the blind, but outside your research department there is a set of double yellow lines ....'

He replied to me in Braille.

*

Note to file: There come times in everyone's life when an act of duplicity, if not hypocrisy, becomes unavoidable. Rather than try to talk your way out of it, as any politician would do, it is far better and more comforting to be completely honest and have a good laugh about it.

Such was inflation at this time in the mid-1970s that prices were escalating at a faster rate than shops were able to dispose of their goods. This caused the government to introduce a regulation which banned shopkeepers from adjusting upwards their price tickets of goods already on the shelves. This action was complemented by the government's establishment of a Price Commission, from which the brewing industry inevitably became targeted: it was still the age of the 'working man's pint', with beer prices being a significant part of the Retail Price Index.

A Price Commission team descended on Bass in Burton with the specific brief to establish the degree to which the company was proving capable to control its costs and prices, in the best public interest.

A headquarters team was arranged to meet the commission, and I was instructed to arrive there exactly one hour after the starting time to take them round the brewery, and explain the current areas of improving operational efficiency, and to discuss any major escalations of cost in the production of beer that were outside our control.

Turning up at the appointed hour, and hearing nothing going on behind the board room door, I knocked gently and walked in, to be confronted by the two teams facing each other in deathly silence, and a look of some relief in the eyes of the teams' chairmen that something had happened to break up an obvious impasse. Whilst totally ignorant of the nature of this awkward state of affairs, I was introduced to the commission team, which consisted of a handful of exactly what one would expect of a band of male civil servants, academics and accountants out to impress a professional organization on its own ground - dressed from city outfit to scruff, but all with blank expressions giving nothing away on their level of expertise on the subjects under examination. However, there was also a most charming woman in the team, immaculately dressed for a good day out, I thought, and carrying no papers. A dark horse not to be underestimated, I thought, despite her distinctive east London accent.

As the tour round the brewery got under way, several of the men showed particular interest in technical details regarding cost control, and the efforts we were making to minimize the effects of inflation on the brewing operation. Each time that they stopped to write copious notes, I observed that the female member was getting further and further behind, and was invariably talking animatedly to a group of brewery operators. This greatly concerned me in case our men were giving her unwittingly a different angle of patter, enough for the commission to question the veracity of my party line being copiously recorded.

At the end of the tour, I was able to talk to her alone and enquired interestedly about what she had been able to pick up during the visit.

"Oh, don't bother about me," she said with a wicked smile, "I'm just a welder's wife from Sarth End [wherever that may be]. Three months ago I saw a packet of corn flakes in a supermarket with three different price stickers on top of each other, bought it and sent it to the Price Commission. A fortnight later I bought a tin of baked beans with two different prices, and sent that to them. You could have blown me down with a feather when they wrote to me offering me a post on the commission, at a thousand quid retainer and all expenses paid! Who else is as lucky as me, getting paid for doing the one thing that I get most enjoyment out of in life - meeting and chatting up blokes?"

Having happily bid them all farewell, I discovered that the first hour in the board room had broken down within minutes, the company team having introduced themselves as pleased to answer any questions the commission wished to put regarding governmental concern about Bass' pricing. The commission had countered that they expected the company first to defend its pricing policy after which they may wish to ask questions. With neither side having done any preparatory work, and the company insisting that they had nothing to defend, at least until they knew what the line of attack was, dialogue had necessarily evaporated. Therefore the commission's report on Bass seemed to depend on their notes taken during the tour of the brewery. When the report arrived, all the achievements and plans that I had described for keeping costs down were listed as negative, and all the issues outside my control were seen as positive contributions to production efficiency and long-term good cost control. On balance, they were pleased to give us a clean bill of health.

*

Note to file: Never deal with a political issue by the use of logic, but it is essential to find out *what* technique to use. Perhaps God (or consultants) will let us know one day.

Another shock to my experiences, not altogether unexpected, was the instruction to get going quickly with the company's 'Management by Objectives' programme (MByO) in the brewery. At last my exposure to God's (or rather some clever rich consultant's) gift to business efficiency and management excellence had arrived. This was occurring four years on from my attendance at business school, where my suspicions had been aroused by the prospect of individual performance and reward being assessed purely against quantified targets.

To me, the problem was what to do about the even more important *non-quantifiable* duties and responsibilities; human relations, for instance, to mention at least ten separate specific areas where weak management skills can easily bring the company to its knees. One could, I supposed, decide on a target maximum number of wildcat strikes - per week, month or year depending on the excellence of the management - as one measured performance: no, the only possibility was to *assume* faultless human relations, and to set quantified targets which would be unattainable in the event of this assumption being false. In this way, even without mentioning them in writing, one has equally to concentrate on these unquantifiable aspects of management.

This reduces any business to a simple list of key result areas, namely those of quantity, quality, timing, cost and profit. All that any section of a company has then to do is to decide which of these apply to them, and then, most importantly, to put them in the most appropriate order of priority.

In the case of a brewery within its normal vertically-integrated company (where the beer is transferred to the sales company at cost), only the first four apply. Without any reference to anyone, I chose the brewery's 'main purpose' as ' to produce the right quality of beer at the right time, in the right volume, at the right cost'. Nobody queried the inferences in that order of priorities, which did not agree with those of the production company chief's objectives for the other 12 breweries. In addition, the corporate strategy, which the business school had told me was such an essential prerequisite to successful MByO, was still mysteriously unavailable in 1974.

Unsurprisingly, MbyO was beginning to appear as nothing more than a wonderful theory for achieving management excellence, sold to and enforced by top management, so long as they did not have to have much to do with it. This feeling was enhanced when I could not think of any measurable objective relevant to *my* performance that did not depend on my whole management team being involved in achieving it.

The only viable solution I could see was to have a unique single MByO programme for the whole brewery management team, eroding somewhat the consistency of the whole company exercise. I did mention this concept to the HQ personnel department, who had presumably been totally involved in setting up MByO in the company, who thought this seemed quite a good idea.

*

One of the most difficult areas of human relations is that of safety in the workplace. This is unquantifiable; for instance, how can one specify *any* acceptable number of accidents (other than zero) in a huge industrial complex with high energy consumption and fast-moving machinery, where there has to be an inevitability of the truly unforeseeable accident? The only possible course of action is that of continuous improvement, and that involves a relationship with the government's local service - the Factory Inspectorate in those days, the Health & Safety Executive today. The brewery, in fact, had an excellent record by existing industry standards, and regularly earned the privilege of flying safety award flags on its flagpoles; this was always slightly worrying, being somewhat inconsistent (at least to anyone unfortunately injured) with our actual performance.

Whatever the performance on safety, it is inevitable that large profitable companies receive disproportionate attention from officialdom, because no such company can afford to be placed in the public eye on such matters, and the public 'knows' that they can afford to pay for all manner of safety improvements. In this way, the local inspector can create far more kudos for himself from the action he demands to be taken by a big brewery than, for instance, in a small sweat shop environment which is so dangerous that the required safety remedies would render the business bankrupt. In general, I recall good relations with the factory inspectors regarding what constituted fair and reasonable safety precautions. However, exactly as with the Excise, the occasional over-enthusiastic, over-ambitious follower of the rulebook had to be dealt with calmly and with dignity.

We were building a new brewhouse some 80 feet high, of steel girder construction covered with corrugated sheeting. We had budgeted £20,000 for scaffolding, which turned out to be insufficient by a factor of three by the time a particularly obnoxious young inspector had finished with us. Every scrap of the building was thick with scaffolding, except for the only girder that no-one needed to go near, going straight across the very top of the building. The inspector arrived one lunchtime to see one of the steeplejacks ambling slowly along the girder above the 80 ft fall, eating his sandwiches. Yelling to him to come down instantly, he demanded of the steeplejack what he thought he was doing on the forbidden girder, informing him that he, his company and Bass would be prosecuted.

Not being sensitive to the niceties of dealing with nasty young inexperienced officious government inspectors, the steeplejack addressed him in the only way he knew how.

"You've made this job so f***ing safe, I was keeping my eye in for the next one," he hissed, jabbing his finger repeatedly into the young man's chest, "now f*** off and don't be seen here again."

Which, to give the young man his due, he did, and wasn't.

Note to file: There are ways and means of educating excessive officialdom and getting away with it. But be selective in your choice of technique, dependent on your personal skills.

With the benefit of hindsight this event was, to me, the first signal of the move towards the nanny State, which appears to have taken us over almost completely at the turn of the millennium. The mid-1970s represented the first generation of adults who knew little or nothing about war, and something had to occur to allow young men to express their natural aggression and to expend that testosterone. What more peaceful way can there be than to become a control freak, telling people that you know far better than them what is good for them; and although backed up by well-intentioned legislation, these laws are unfortunately always capable of ludicrous interpretation by the fanatical do-gooder.

At the millennium, the second generation of post-war adults is well settled in, having been taught little or nothing about the great wars, and having experienced the development of the nanny State into a world of human rights without, apparently, any need for associated duties and responsibilities towards one's fellow human beings. It is not necessary to look much further for the roots of institutionalized delinquency.

*

Note to file: The next time you come up against an ignorant, aggressive little tin god trying to dictate the way you run your life, just bear in mind that if there was a world war on he/she wouldn't be there. And surely this is better than a war?

In the mid-1970s, the trades unions had barely come out of the dark ages, at least in the sense of failing to acknowledge the value of the steady improvement, in the post-war years, in the quality of life of those working in manufacturing industry. Certainly in profitable and responsible companies, considerable progress had been made towards a 'fair share of the cake' for all, including the general easing of working conditions. However, the concept of our current property-owning democracy was still only nascent, and anathema to the trades unions and average worker. However, these factors were clearly just beginning to erode the hard-line 'them and us' attitudes dictated by union officials and reinforced by them in all negotiations with companies.

In the annual negotiations in our Burton brewery, therefore, money was the only item the union was prepared to discuss.

In this routine, I was invariably part horrified and part amused at the regular arguments put forward by the local union official; horrified by his selection of whatever staple food (such as potatoes) was going up faster than inflation in that year, to justify a larger wage increase to prevent starvation of his members; yet amused by his deep sincerity in representing members in this way, whose wages were probably at least twice as much as his union salary.

Such was the routine, invariably ending up at a wage increase appropriate to the rate of inflation, and also to the guidelines (you-will-obey type) from the HQ personnel. They, of course, had the thankless task of maintaining some sort of wage consistency between the dozen or so annual brewery negotiations in the Bass Charrington group.

It was not this routine, perhaps best described as a ritual, that attracted my interest, but the progress that could be made outside the annual wage negotiation. I had already determined in Manchester that something needed to be done to advance the development of the abilities and talents in the unionised workforce, repressed by their union's vested interest in retaining the distinction between 'them and us'. But it had to be done away from, but not be incompatible with, the rigid central control of HQ personnel.

Thus was concocted a master plan with, and largely by, the best personnel manager I had the pleasure to work with. Peter was not an expert graduate theoretician such as one finds in HQs, most of whom had never rubbed shoulders with a shop floor, but a man who understood what makes people tick. The plan, quite simply, was to adopt a policy of demonstrating to the workforce that it should not be *necessary* for them to be a member of a trade union, largely by providing working conditions and opportunities that no local union branch would ever be authorized to try to negotiate.

The mid-1970s was not the best time to start such a project; the Labour Government was enforcing more and more legislation in favour of union power, such as TULRA (Trade

Union Labour Relations Act), on the pretext of it being good for industry. In addition, moves were afoot towards adopting the European practice of employee participation in important company affairs. This was not the best thing for Britain, I thought, because we would be bound to do it strictly by the rulebook, while continental industry would continue to implement it only as far as it suited them.

Peter had told me not to worry about TULRA or any other such legislation, because it really only applied to backward companies. He understood exactly what the government's intentions were on the subject and assured me that our approach to labour relations in the brewery were, and would always be, ahead of any laws. Let HQ worry about TULRA if they wanted to.

Other countries' practices and laws, however, were a different kettle of fish for the future, so we thought we would start off our policy by inviting the brewery's union convenor (the most senior shop steward) to become a member of the brewery management committee, and thus become directly involved in strategic local decision-making and planning.

Such a drastic conflict with his 'them and us' discipline inevitably forced him politely to decline, but the first critical point had been made, registered and, to a degree, scored.

*

Note to file: Always open a long-term strategy with an impossibly 'ideal' objective, but which illustrates the essence of what might become possible.

The next move was to publicize the three-year capital expenditure plan, and, as a priority, to invite the whole workforce to become involved in those major investments that we had included for improving their working conditions. Specifically, they were asked to put into sequence, year by year, three projects, each costing roughly half a million pounds, offering a new canteen, top quality changing and rest rooms, and a medical centre.

To everyone's utter amazement, the medical centre was voted, by a large majority, as the priority for Year 1. As progress developed on construction on the brewery site, a workforce committee was able to become involved in peripheral decision making. The most important subject appeared to be the role of the brewery first-aiders in emergencies when the centre was unmanned, including availability of transport to the local hospital.

Despite our suggestion that the traditional method of calling an ambulance from the hospital (only 200 yards away) was likely to be as fast as an even more local arrangement, our commitment to employee involvement left us no choice but to agree to their enthusiastic wishes. They chose the vehicle that would be the easiest in which to load a hospital case, namely a London taxi; this was quite well thought out really, being the only available vehicle fitted with front-opening doors. Interestingly, in the ensuing years, I cannot recall anyone ever enquiring why there was a rusting taxi sitting at the side of the smart medical centre.

*

Note to file: Stand by to be surprised when you start something like true consultation, but never show it.

Further government interference in the mid 1970s involved mutterings at high level that advertising alcoholic products should be banned. Matters such as these would always inspire Sir into his lateral thinking mode, in this case coming up with the brilliant idea of acquiring some shire horses. His logic was that the showing of heavy horses at national and county shows invariably attracted television coverage, and what an opportunity to do up some of the old horse-drawn drays being collected from around the group for the forthcoming Bass Museum of Brewing History.

Bass had long foregone horses as a way of delivering beer, in fact since the predominance of the internal combustion engine in the late 1920s superseding steam wagons. In the early 1930s, the remaining 300 brewery horses in Burton were transferred to the tender care and responsibility of the engineering department. Two years later there were only three. But now, there was a chance to restore a wonderful heritage by rejoining the heavy horse world, still dominated by a few of the other major breweries. These included the Whitbread heavy horses used in the annual Lord Mayor of London's parade, Courage's famous stables in Reading, and other companies competing in the heavy horse events at the nation's showgrounds.

This revival was not intended to inspire any changes to the modern method of delivering beer, leaving the use of working horses (to this day) to one or two of the smaller breweries, which have a plethora of their pubs concentrated in a small urban area around the brewery. This allows efficient deliveries in terms of barrels per horse-mile (what a splendid example of an MByO objective to set), as well as equally useful advertisement, and, most importantly, less intolerant traffic wardens. Young's brewery in Wandsworth is the classic example of this continuing use of heavy horses.

However, Bass' acquisition of shires and smart wagons more or less demanded their part use in Burton town for delivering beer as a major public relations exercise, and thus the accountants (bless them) become involved in this venture. They told us that horses used for show are capital assets, but horses used for delivering beer are revenue items, and ne'er the twain shall meet. There was no mention of what the horses might think about this.

Note to file: There is nothing better than keeping accountants in useful employment by giving them an insoluble challenge to ponder over.

Unfortunately, this was not the end of the matter. Having been told, after lengthy consideration and consultation, that the horses would be treated as capital assets, it was necessary to establish a capital budget for their acquisition, plus forward authorization for necessary replacements in the event of sudden death (not uncommon in young heavy horses) or other unforeseen debilitations. The first instance of a sudden death required an urgent search throughout the shire horse world for an exact match to replenish the show team; this was not an easy task when colour and markings of the horses need to be virtually identical in team competitions. Having found a perfect replacement, and the head horseman knowing only the ritual method of purchasing in the horse world, the deal was fixed by the slapping of hands.

However, finding instant funds from a large corporation proved an equally difficult task. Rushing back to Burton to acquire the money from Sir, who had conveniently slipped £3,000 into the annual capital budget for such a contingency, Sir's secretary told the PR manager in charge of the shires that Sir was away for a fortnight, and in view of the obvious urgency sent her to the finance director.

"I can only issue you with a cheque countersigned by Sir," he pontificated.

"But he's away for a fortnight," pleaded the PR girl, "and our name will be mud in the horse world if we are unable to pay, after having slapped hands on the deal."

"May I remind you that a limited company cannot slap hands," retorted the FD. (A little bit of *deja vu* from a previous clash with accountants, in an earlier chapter, I recall). "You will just have to wait until Sir returns."

Note to file: Confirmation received that accountants *are* condoms on the spearhead of progress.

An expensive damage limitation exercise saved the day, by informing the horse world that in future we would always pay top price for a show horse, but in view of the early death we had suffered, further purchases would have to be based on two veterinary reports (which would also give enough time to screw the money out of the finance department).

*

With the formation of the Bass Charrington group and the consequent decline of paternalistic interest in the individual families' beer businesses, some measure of overall cohesion had been established by regular annual visits by the group chairman to all the regions. In this way, at least the opinion-forming employees had a chance to listen to company policy from the horse's mouth, to talk with the top boss over a glass of beer on issues that they thought important for the directors to be aware of, and to be reassured of the ongoing success of the business. It was also an opportunity to clean and polish up the brewery site for this annual 'parade'.

As the budgeting of maintenance costs got more and more scrutinized by the accountants, it became more and more difficult to justify the high cost of redecorating the brewery, let alone the whole of the chairman's long route through the site, for this one annual visit. Someone had the bright idea of repainting only the visible sides of the hundreds of supporting pillars on the prescribed brewery route; but when the chairman obliged by commenting on how expensive his visits were in terms of suits ruined by wet paint, the natural extension was to assume that the chairman ought to welcome having his breweries presented to him in their natural everyday state. Thus was born the informal welcoming visit, rather than a parade, which we were not slow in using to best advantage.

The first thing we did was to take the chairman off the usual route, to meet the senior trade union employees alone, on their own habitual meeting ground. If our plan to involve them more in the affairs of the brewery was to bear fruit, nothing could be better than the chance for the chairman to treat them as equals, in their own territory and vice versa.

Things could easily have gone wrong, despite Peter's lengthy preparatory homework with the union convenor. A particularly nasty piece of Labour legislation had just come in, enforcing companies to publish in their annual reports not only the details of all directors' remuneration, but also the number of employees receiving salaries in excess of, I think, £20,000. This was the politics of envy *par excellence*, clearly attempting to illustrate to the masses the degree of greedy exploitation of the workers by the bosses. In fact, in Bass Charrington's case, of the relatively small number of earners above that figure (out of 30,000 or so employees), there was a fair sprinkling of 'workers'! This was never revealed officially, presumably for fear of a backlash from the whole range of employees.

In the year that I just squeezed into the bottom bracket, I decided to test Sir on my position in the company.

"Is it right, sir, that there should be 44 staff in the company that are more important than me, when I am responsible for churning out 5 per cent of all the beer produced in the UK?"

"Yes," he replied.

Note to file: When you have a charismatic leader as your boss, you get to know pretty well exactly where you are with him.

In chairmen's positions, however, it was potentially extremely embarrassing to expose themselves to a unionized group in possession of such personal information, that was made available solely for the underlying purpose of stirring up aggression and conflict (the government would say 'change').

Fortunately, the private meeting between our chairman and union representatives was a huge success and generated a high level of respect that held over in subsequent years, when he was able to hold open question-and-answer sessions with employees on any subject without a single riposte of a political or personal nature.

It is probable that this piece of legislation was a trigger for a noticeable swing away from personal contact between top boss and worker in industry generally, in favour of consultant-designed soporific video presentations of company messages that burdened my latter working years.

Note to file: Respect, understanding and interest for people on their own territory gives the best chance of gaining respect in return.

The informality of these visits may or may not have been influential in the development of a favourite stopping place on the annual tour, namely the medical centre that the brewery employees were so interested in. It may have been a coincidence that it was always the same nurse on duty, but she had invariably prepared an interesting subject to attract the chairman's interest. On the first occasion, the chairman volunteered to be guinea pig to a recently acquired eye-testing machine.

"Chairman, were you aware that you have a slightly lazy left eye?" she enquired.

"That's funny," he replied, with a wide grin, "I went to my optician last week who told me that I had a lazy *right* eye! Never mind, keep up the good work."

The following year, she had decided to talk about the centre's key involvement in the company's executive medical programme, in which all the basic examinations, tests and sampling were carried out in the centre before the candidate got a good going over by a local medical consultant.

"I am pleased to report, chairman, that 59 per cent of all the executives in Burton have had executive medicals," she announced proudly.

"I thought they were compulsory," thundered the chairman, "on second thoughts I can't think why; it doesn't half run the risk of slowing up the company's succession plan. Have you had one, Bob?" turning to me.

"Well, er, chairman…" I started, trying to think of something to say which did not reveal me as a non-believer in such matters. I promised to think about it.

As the following annual visit loomed, I worried a little as to whether he had remembered my promise, and I decided to undergo the experience, just to be on the safe side.

"How many units of alcohol do you drink in a week?" was the first obvious question to be asked of a brewer by the nurse. My God, I thought, why hadn't I anticipated this and found out what was a reasonable figure to quote that would not raise any suspicion, disbelief or panic?

"How does 50 grip you?" I suggested to the nurse after a moment's thought.

"Mr. Ricketts, you are the first executive honestly to admit to being on the slippery slope," she replied in a tone of great concern.

I decided not to confuse the nurse with too many facts about the real world, but I did make a note to keep a record of my consumption. Fortunately, I had been invited to a bankers' dinner that night, and discovered there that financial people beat brewers at the drinking game by such a large margin that I didn't have to worry in the slightest about my own drinking habits. It should be noted that it is not everyone in a brewery who sinks 14 pints in a day, but readers can be assured that William Hague's famous revelation of comparable consumption as a drayman was far from being uncommon in the 1980s.

Note to file: It never pays to try to correct a professional who has been trained (or brainwashed) into drawing dogmatic textbook conclusions about people's health.

The next event of major recall in the course of my executive medical was the examination by the consultant. Imagination might be required by the non-cognoscenti regarding the internal procedure that one had to go through, without anaesthetic,so as to be told that all the vital organs were of the right size, shape and consistency. No way was I going to go through that again, whatever the chairman ordered.

At my final interview, confidentially with my own doctor,

he told me that he had diagnosed from the report that all I needed was an aspirin a day. Enquiring why, he said firstly that it would do me no harm, and secondly that it would teach me a lesson for having an executive medical; and by the way, was I going to give up beer or smoking?

In response to such a stupid question to a brewer, my family suffered hell from months of my nicotine withdrawal; but whilst writing this tale, I am passing proudly through the 200000 hours barrier (and still counting).

I have no wish from this account to discourage anyone from taking up the offer of a free company medical; of all the hundreds, if not thousands of Bass Charrington executive medicals, there *had been* a known recorded case of a life-threatening condition being spotted of which the candidate was totally ignorant.

When checking my experiences with my peers, one of the regional brewery directors encouraged me with the story of his. He was a dapper, short, tubby Dickensian character, a man in total self-assured control of his brewery operation, having flown 'Stringbag' torpedo aircraft at sea in the first years of the Second World War- there is little more brave or foolhardy person than that – ending the war in the Pacific in a brewery ship providing morale-boosting refreshment to the troops. In the ensuing years he then became an expert in a variety of subjects; certainly in my experience there seemed very little that he did not know about Majorca, jewels and the historic buildings of the City of London. I mention these experiences, interests and mild eccentricities only as a possible cause or explanation for this tale, which I reproduce more or less word for word as he told it to me:

Consultant Physician: 'I have the results of your executive medical here, and I have to tell you that I have taken the precaution of having an ambulance standing by, because I do not wish to have you dying in my consulting room. Your cholesterol level is higher than any I have seen in the whole of my medical career; it requires instant treatment, so you will be able to go straight to hospital in the ambulance, into a regime that I have prepared for you there, as soon as we have finished our discussion. To ensure that the regime is exactly right for you, would you please tell me something about your alcohol habits?'

Brewery Director: 'Where would you like me to start?'

CP: 'How about Monday?'

BD: 'Well, I go into the brewery and clear my desk by 9.30, then I tour the brewery, stopping at the lab to do the day's official taste test, and end up in the sample store to check the 30 or so sample casks of the beers that are on sale in the pubs. By this time an allied trader or other business visitor has arrived by appointment, so we have a couple of beers before I suggest a sampling visit to two or three pubs on the way to lunch. At the restaurant a couple of gin and tonics and a bottle of wine followed by a Gaelic coffee is the norm. After lunch we go to the boardroom, where we do the necessary business over a Scotch or two until it is time for Badger [chauffeur] to take the visitor to the station (they nearly always come by train, I'm not sure why) and then me to my home. My wife and I enjoy gin and tonics before a supper over a bottle of wine, and brandy or liqueurs before bed; that is unless I am out in the trade, when, of course, I have to drink with our customers'.

CP: 'OK, what about the rest of the week?'

BD: 'Pretty well identical, really.'

CP: 'The weekends as well?'

BD: 'Good heavens no! I visit a few pubs on Saturday, but my wife and I either entertain friends in the evening or are invited out, and we drink no more than you would expect at such social occasions, more or less as I have described for a typical working lunch. On Sunday I take my wife out to a few pubs before lunch at a nice restaurant where we enjoy cocktails and a typical meal with wine and Gaelic coffee.

CP: 'Thank you, for that. I have only one more question. Are you telling me the truth?'

BD: 'Let me think.....I suppose it's possible that I've left something out.'

Three days into his enforced regime in the hospital he suddenly realized that his health was deteriorating at such a rate that he had to do something about it pretty quickly. Feeling like death on the fourth day, he sneaked unnoticed out of the hospital, and immediately told his doctor what had happened. His doctor, who knew his habits and state of health backwards, sympathetically suggested that he had done exactly the right thing to return to his 'normal' way of life, but what about paying lip service to the concern of the consultant, by disposing of the whisky stock in the boardroom? He did, and replaced it with gin.

A few years later he retired, taking up the executive version of Voluntary Service Overseas, touring the globe to help third world countries set up drink (and other) factories and businesses. He eventually died at a grand age that any of us would be grateful to reach.

Note to file: There is only one person in the world to decide what is good for you. You.

CHAPTER 9

THINGS FOREIGN AND ROYAL

The late 1970s were characterized by an accelerating swing away from ales to lagers (although it was to be some time before lager achieved 50 per cent of the market), combined with a further concentration of the brewing industry, and the arrival of a right-wing government. Hopes amongst British industrial managers were at last directed towards control of union power, and they were not to be disappointed over the ensuing years, but other factors antagonistic to the brewing industry were beginning to come into play.

The British beer market was beginning to be swamped by continental lager brands, most of them brewed in the UK but marketed as if imported. At that stage, they tended to fall into two categories, either inferior products in terms of strength or inferior products in terms of flavour. The former were characteristic of high-volume well-known continental brands franchised to our big brewing companies, but in a much weaker form: the relatively extortionate UK beer duty, plus the required advertising expenditure and royalty payments, could not possibly add up to an acceptable retail price at the bar for an ordinary non-premium European lager. The latter category was characteristic of smaller brewing companies who did not have the resources to adapt their breweries to all the requirements for good lager brewing.

One must never be too critical of any beer that sells well; by definition, a popular product must have some good qualities. However, wry smiles were seen in brewing circles when the Excise laid down a minimum original gravity below which beer could not be called beer, and at least one very well-known continental brand had to have its strength increased.

All this did not matter too much in the early years of lager popularity. The hot summer of 1976 caused an unmanageable increase in demand for lager; Bass reacted to its inability to produce enough Carling lager (at that time one of the few big-selling standard lagers at a 'proper' strength / original gravity) by installing, between pub cellar and bar, in-line lager chillers on the keg *ales* as well. The problem was solved; we had discovered what I had always suspected, that much of the public was not really interested in lager itself, but *cold* beer. In fact, we had numerous complaints that the ale tasted too much like lager.

This finding scotched somewhat the established universal marketing rationale that the public was acquiring a *taste* for continental beers on their holidays, when the reasoning should have been based on *temperature*. Sadly, this new concept was either ignored or dismissed by our own marketing department, who continued to feel a weakness in our beer portfolio should the public insist on their lagers being of authentic European origin. For this reason we, the brewers, were horrified to be told that a deal had been secretly struck with a famed continental brewery to brew their beer in Burton alongside (and in competition with) our main Carling and Tennents brands.

Note to file: Important high-level decisions, involving several sections of a business, are best arrived at through consultation down to the 'doer' level. This never happens. At least until it is too late.

It is difficult to describe the full horror of a team of arrogant young men, trained in the art of their own peculiar ways of doing things in a faraway foreign land, telling the best brewers in England how to produce a quality of beer that they would never have dared to sell in their own country, to a technical specification completely unsuited to the British market. Yes, we had also fallen into the trap of having a new ultra-weak lager (we could just call it that), but this time among a portfolio of the best in the land, and this foreign product was so important that all the beer recovered from the process, like tail ends of pumping and yeast pressings, had to be added back to *our* beers! (The concept of charging huge British Excise duties *before* the beer is made, with the consequent need to save every scrap of beer possible during the process, was completely alien to them).

In addition, reciprocation of the faultless manners and politeness of these people made things even more difficult to bear.

The preparatory work for such a major franchise operation was necessarily lengthy. Whilst the poor brewers had their brewery turned upside down, repiped, retanked and fitted with all manner of alien gadgetry to allow for their medieval traditional processes, the marketeers were away doing all the things that they assured us could only be done in a foreign city.

They did come home from time to time, laden with all manner of freebies to support the market launch. The popularity of the tracksuits (with logos) in the local school generated much demand long before the first brew was put in; school seemed a strange consumer target, I thought.

Seasoned with jealousy because we, the brewers, had not been invited to see the franchiser's brewery (nor the foreign city), we had to hold our first technical brewing conference with the franchiser in downtown Burton, which went something like this:

Us: 'Looking at your brewing specification, we have to tell you that the specified gas content of your lager in keg is too high. The beer will become nothing but froth when dispensed from the keg into a glass.'

Them: 'Why? You agreed to the specification.'

Us: 'We didn't, this is the first time we have seen it.'

Them: 'Your negotiators for the franchise agreed to it.'

Us: 'There must be some scope for discussion between the technical experts, on minor but key items that will affect the customer?'

Them: 'There is no discussion on the agenda; that is our Europe-wide specification.'

Us: 'The beer will be unsaleable in our pubs.'

Them: 'Nonsense. This standard works well all over Europe.'

Us: 'Our pubs are very different. We have state-of the-art dispensing of draught beer, designed to deliver a pint of lager in 11 seconds, and we also have a unique law that says exactly one pint must be delivered. The reason for the high speed of dispense is that in many pubs 50 per cent of sales take place in the last 15 minutes before the pub closes. Your beer will have far too much gas in it to allow for these requirements.'

Them: 'This is a simple target, well within our skills.'

Us: 'Where can we see this skill in operation?'

Them: 'Come and see it in our own pubs!'

Objective No.1 had been achieved, namely an invitation for my brewers to visit their wonderful city, and on top of that, to experience their *post*-state-of-the-art technology!

We were warmly welcomed and went to the first pub:

Them: 'This is the first of the six pubs in the city that sells keg beer, so we will be able to see them all.'

Us: 'That is interesting. We expected a lot more. In England we have some tens of thousands of lager dispense units. And by the way, what is that barman doing with that ice cream spatula in his hand?'

Them: 'It is standard issue, not often used.'

Us: 'He is now scooping foam out of the glass with it, presumably to get more beer in..... I have timed him at two minutes so far and the stein still isn't full.'

Them: 'Let us go to another pub, this one is not typical.'

-

Us: 'Plastic spatulas seem to be pretty standard equipment in this pub as well.'
Them: 'They are, but rarely used.'
Us: 'Would it be possible to have a talk with the pub manager?'
Them: 'Of course. You can ask him anything.'
Us: 'As the manager, do you have financial controls and service targets to work to?'
Manager: 'Of course. What is it that interests you?'
Us: 'On average, how long does it take to fill a half-litre stein?'
Manager: 'It depends how lively the beer is. It is not important. Perhaps two minutes.'
Us: 'How many litres of beer are you expected to sell for every 100 litres delivered from the brewery?'
Manager: '150.'
Us: 'Thank you. In England we would probably be put in prison for that.'

-

Us: 'I think it is time for us to have another little discussion about how we are going to dispense your beer in England, don't you think?'
Them: 'That is not necessary. What you have seen is not typical. I will engage the resources of our technical research department and ensure that your requirements can be guaranteed. Meantime, we will start brewing the beer together in Burton in two weeks as planned, and your problem will be resolved by the time that the beer is ready to be sold.'

Note to file: Times come when you need to recognize when to stop bashing your head against a brick wall, but you must still go on behaving like a gentleman. It is surprising how quickly things can

162

resolve themselves if the other side is left to find out for itself the stubbornness of its ways. (In this case they didn't – perhaps this doesn't work with foreigners).

With the saviour of British beer dispense techniques of the late 1970s in their foreign hands, more important things were afoot as we got used to their archaic brewing techniques. After a few weeks, we were allowed to brew the beer without their expert supervision, as long as we flew samples across the North Sea every week for analysis and flavour evaluation.

This was the start of a constant flow of subtle criticism to keep us in our place, with never-ending complaints that there was room for improvement up to their standards. It was never explained how they possessed established standards for such a weak beer, made nowhere else in the world.

As time went on, the flow of samples necessarily became less frequent because the beer had filled the pub cellars and largely remained unsold because it dispensed as nothing but foam. The franchiser's research department finally produced a new dispense tap of their own design for handling their high-gas beers in Britain, which turned out to be useless.

At the height of this crisis, the head brewer came to me to admit that some of the beer had been brewed accidentally at too high a level of bitterness, and was far too weak and bitter for blending away into our own beers; and in view of the miserable performance in the pubs, it unfortunately represented about six weeks' sales. Not yet being computerized, the solution to the problem was devised twice as quickly, on the back of a cigarette packet:

"If you water one of our lagers down to their strength, and blend it 50:50 into theirs, you will achieve the correct specification," I suggested. The only reaction we received was that the samples submitted during the following weeks were reported back as 'much improved', at least until Murphy's Law came into play, through none other than the mouth of our chief accountant.

"Please help me, Bob," he started, "I have to report to the franchiser not only the volume of beer sold, but also the volume brewed, and the figures don't seem to add up."

"It's not something you would understand," I said, "just make sure you quote the right sales figure for their royalty payment, and give them a suitable figure for the brewings."

"It's not as simple as that."

"I'll speak to Sir about it, then come back to you."

Note to file: Resolution: I must stop making notes about accountants. Are they all the same, all the time?

The ensuing fracas was neatly superseded by our company's realization that the reciprocal deal with the franchiser to promote our beer in *their* country was effectively being ignored, so would it not be sensible to cease the franchise on the grounds of mutual incompatibility? In this way we luckily escaped from one of the most ridiculous deals undertaken by any company, that not only had a superfluity of successful own brands in the first place, but also was laying itself open to all the effects of promoting an inferior product.

I genuinely believe that there is no wind that blows nobody any good. We were left with a vast surplus of expensive tanks capable of a disproportionate expansion of British-style beer processing, thus ensuring the long-term future of the Burton brewery as one of the biggest and most efficient in the country.

*

In line with all the excitement over lager expanding its sales at the expense of both cask and keg ales, CAMRA was getting more and more vocal in its resistance to the decline of warm, flat cask beer. It was placing the blame on the big brewers' lager advertising campaigns, rather than accepting that a proportion of beer drinkers were actually beginning to *prefer* cold, pale, more highly gassed beers, whilst others were preferring the more consistent keg ales.

CAMRA had started to run successful beer festivals around the country, consisting of the promotion and consumption of all the local cask beers, but with emphasis on the smaller producers. The campaign was swinging more and more heavily against the big bad brewers 'dictating and monopolising the market to their own financial ends'.

However, on the tenet that all news about beer is good news, because it stimulates interest and discussion amongst thirsty aficionado customers, our public relations people encouraged us to become involved locally: after all, Bass was still the biggest brewer of cask beer in the world, with at least a dozen very successful regional and national brands, with every intention of staying in that position. But it did stick in the gullet when we sponsored some of their festivals to the tune of several thousand pounds each, only to be harangued by the opening speaker for being a leading destroyer of everything that the customer (or was it CAMRA?) stood for.

My opportunity to test the water came when a team from CAMRA visited the Burton brewery, and of course the sample store. It was difficult for them to be too rude whilst surrounded by 200 sample casks, each representing several hundred barrels of cask beer currently being sold in pubs across the country. I decided to select the weirdest of the bearded weirdos amongst the gang - not the easiest of tasks - and politely asked him if it was true that CAMRA, as I had been told by someone, was dominated by half a dozen left-wing Hammersmith intellectuals.

"Say no more, Bob, I'm one of them," he replied, equally politely.

*

Note to file: Left-wing politics and fanaticism seem to go hand-in-hand. You need to worry even more if intellectuals are involved as well. And what to expect if they come from Hammersmith as well?

Meanwhile, the planned elimination of left-wing class war attitudes among the brewery workforce (the 'sleepers' were there, but identified and well monitored) was moving forward progressively outside the annual negotiation ritual, with the introduction of more ideas to make life easier and more satisfying on the shop floor.

The increasing disposable income of our operators, manifested in the1970s in the form of a new car-owning democracy, was recognised by equality of access and parking facilities; other simple initiatives, like paying detailed attention to rotating the most boring, repetitive jobs, helped us on our way. However, the concept of doing away with clocking on and off, in return for staying on until one's shift relief arrived, was a major innovation for that time, involving for the first time the concept of a mutual responsibility for the efficient running of the brewery.

Payment of wages directly into a bank was offered, instead of the normal undignified queuing for a packet of cash every week; however, the legal requirement for wages to be available weekly in cash remained virtually sacrosanct amongst union officials, if only for ease of collecting union subscriptions. This move also disposed of the ease of extracting strike fund money from the members, at the time of any advance planning of industrial mayhem.

The company as a whole was also beginning to stir on the question of equality among all the employees. The first issue was discrimination on pension benefits, where long servers could not qualify for their years in the paternalistic past, because their scheme had been non-contributory, with pensions paid only at the discretion of the directors.

The company was also working up a scheme for universal communication, consultation and participation, whereby everyone would have the chance to make their contribution to the running of the company. The company would communicate issues to its employees, consultation on these would take place locally, and participation would be by feedback.

Within a week the word participation was changed to involvement, after someone pointed out that, in Europe, 'participation' inferred the establishment of supervisory boards of worker directors! This well-intentioned scheme for levelling the playing field between 'them' and 'us' was to become a sore test over the next decade. This was particularly difficult for the plethora of 'paternal dictators' among the management: many of them had enough trouble getting as far as consulting their employees about the decisions they had already taken.

*

Note to file: Have you noticed how often directors exempt themselves from the wonderful schemes that they have ordered for improving the efficiency of the company?

A highlight of the late 1970s in the Burton brewery was a royal visit. Bass in particular had a long history of royal connections, starting with King Edward VII's visits to the Bass family home and 'mashing-in' the famous King's Ale in 1902, followed by the Prince of Wales brewing the Prince's Ale in 1928. Exactly 50 years later we were to be honoured by a visit from HRH Princess Anne.

Agreement on a programme for royal approval was through discussion with the offices of the Lord Lieutenant and Chief Constable. The obvious possibility of mashing-in a Princess Ale was raised at the preliminary visit of their representatives, to which the stuffed shirt of the two said how undignified such a process would be, let alone the indignity of having to climb an open staircase to get to the mash room; this was completely unacceptable.

Leaving him huffing and puffing as the tour round the proposed route progressed, the police chief whispered in my ear not to take any notice of the old duffer; from past experience he was certain that the Princess would be more than happy to do the whole proposed programme.

"Why are you not having wives present at the welcoming line-up?" enquired the policeman later on.

"I don't know why," I replied, "but I was told by the main board director-in-charge that we wouldn't. Why do you ask?"

"Wives are nearly always there at companies' welcoming line-ups."

"Why?" I asked innocently.

"It's obvious; so they can get a new outfit on company expenses!" came the reply of great experience.

That evening I reported to the director-in-charge, none other than the Smiling Hatchet Man (SHM), that I proposed to submit our original programme, despite the reservations of one of the parties, to which he agreed. I then passed on the policeman's tip regarding wives, to be met by a hollow laugh and a disconnected line.

In due course, royal approval for the tour, including the mashing-in of a Princess Ale, came through, at the same time as a local phone message. There was a change of mind; yes, we would have wives at the line-up, and yes, my wife could have an outfit on company expenses. This generosity of SHM was somewhat unexpected, but mysteriously appeared to be linked to an urgency to keep strictly to the scheduled timing of the tour. This became clear when, knowing of his passion for horse racing, I discovered that the event was to take place on Derby Day, and that the royal tour was due to finish only 15 minutes before the 'off'. Obviously this was barely enough time to guarantee being able to get to a warmed-up television set in the directors' mess, without a bit of pressure on the leading participants to keep the tour to schedule.

The great day came. This was at a time when our royalty was at a peak of public esteem, willingly carrying out undiminished public duties despite security scares involving personal attack. The welcome and appreciation of the employees' families set the scene for a wonderful visit.

The Princess had clearly been well briefed on our business. It shone through in her conversation and interest in the employees that she met, and she gave the impression of thoroughly enjoying the visit, including the mashing-in of her Princess Ale. A superb time was had by all, including SHM, who, despite the visit starting 10 minutes late, was able to get to his beloved Derby.

Note to File: Must find out why royalty seem to be surrounded by an impermeable barrier of establishment hangers-on and formality, of no significance in the modern world. Perhaps it is the hangers-on who have the vested interest in maintaining *their* pretence of superiority and remoteness from the common herd.

When a good friend of mine, who had wangled himself into the brewery crowd, went home, the one thing his wife wanted to know was what she had been wearing. He had to tell her that he had forgotten, but Mrs. Ricketts looked a dream!

Subsequently, I learned that I was the only one in the welcoming line-up who had been told by SHM that a new wife's outfit on the company had been allowed. When I submitted my monthly expenses to Sir, who had been given no understanding of the arrangement despite being in the line-up himself, he immediately enquired of SHM the nature of the claim. The validity was confirmed, except that no woman could possibly spend more than £100 on an outfit, whatever the occasion! (translated to the beginning of the new millennium, this equates to approximately £250).

Note to file: Forget the old paternalistic ignorance of how others live. Modern top management is just as bad.

In retrospect, nothing could have been more fortunate than being directly involved in running such an event: to get at least a measly £100 (plus VAT) added another dollop of cream on top of it all. A year later, the Princess Ale had matured and was ready for bottling. Not having done this kind of thing for 50 years, we had opted for imitating past practice as closely as possible; this involved specially manufactured bottles with wax covering over cork closures.

The extent of the historical importance of the beer business to Burton had been highlighted at Bass' bicentenary in 1977, when we decided to give most of the remaining bottles of the 1869 brew to long-serving brewery employees. It involved replacing the labels, most of which had decayed over the 108 years in storage. The labels themselves were overprinted standard Bass labels for 1869, the design being of a complexity to compete with modern banknotes, in order to discourage other brewers copying the company's unique trade marks acquired in 1865. We received a quotation of £1500 for making the printing blocks, and £15 for printing them! That is, until we discovered that the oldest printer in town still had the original blocks in full working order!

It was clearly important that the Princess Ale had to compete well with the technology of 1869, but we were stymied from the start, trying to find a modern wax that was flexible enough to remain intact around the top of the bottle, without the risk of cracking or crazing after a long time.

My solution was to go modern. Sir was about to take his team on a trip to the company's chateau in Margaux, the epicentre of the finest Grand Cru clarets. I told the head brewer to continue the wax search, whilst I would find out what the First Growth Chateaux did about sealing their bottles for laying down over the next 100 years, and we would compare notes on my return.

I was amazed to be told at two famous chateaux that the normal commercial Viskring-type of protective covering was quite sufficient for laying down the wine indefinitely. By coincidence SHM appeared at one of our dinners where I suggested to him that our problem at the brewery could be resolved by imitating these great wine experts.

"Just because that is good enough for a First Growth Chateau doesn't mean that it is good enough for Bass," he roared, "go back and find the right wax!"

*

Note to file: Be grateful for all the helpful bits of advice you get from on high.

In other respects, things were going well at the brewery. However, I had been thrown out of the directors' mess along with the managing director of the local trading company (which ran the pubs and sold beer to the free trade), on the grounds that 'doers' were incompatible with whatever the senior ivory tower people needed to keep to themselves when in relaxed mode. Their egos?

Fortunately, my fellow exile invited me to join his own mess elsewhere in the town, where it was possible to enjoy much more stimulating company. Significant voluntary efforts were made by a good friend to have me reinstated as a matter of principle, to the point of asking for this to be his retirement present. The eventual reply was:

'We agree in principle, but if we do that we will have to let *all* the rubbish in!'

The meaning of this became clear when I *did* receive an invitation to rejoin, at exactly the same time that the senior ivory tower personnel people had upgraded themselves to directors' mess status.

Note to file: Keep your eyes and ears open all the time as to where you really are within the hierarchy.

The embarrassment of all this was assuaged by a further invitation, namely to do the same job as my fellow mess exile, in the 'trade', in a different part of the country. Following the announcement, and bearing in mind the marketing director's eviction from the brewery sample store, I decided to test the humour of the keeper of the sample store on my next visit by asking for a gin and tonic. He had one all ready.

CHAPTER 10

MANAGEMENT IN THE COMMERCIAL JUNGLE

By 1980, the beer business still maintained the structure of half a dozen major pub-owning players ('The Big 6') and a wealth of regional and local brewers. The six were Bass, Allied, Whitbread, Watney, Scottish & Newcastle and Courage, with more than 70 per centof the market. Guinness, as producer and supplier of its brands to all the pubs in the UK, added a further 10 per cent to the 'big' total.

The whole public debate of cask versus keg ales, and keg ales versus keg lager, was equally in a state of some commercial stability; this could be witnessed through the provision of all these varieties in the vast majority of public houses, in accordance with the demand of local customers. Needless to say, this did not please everybody.

The first issue was political, in terms of monopoly.Although the largest brewer (Bass) still had only 22 per cent of the UK market, this was considered by some to be excessive. In talks with the government, this had been crystallised down to genuine concern about some *local* dominations by a single brewer, mainly as a result of the major concentration of the industry over the previous 25 years. Out of this, the industry agreed to a voluntary substantial pub swap with each other, to reduce these local dominations.

The second issue concerned the continuing onslaught from CAMRA on the major brewers' advertising and promotional campaigns for lager: to them, the big bad brewers were quite clearly still aiming at the destruction of their beloved warm flat beer heritage.

Note to file: Always remember that fanatics cannot accept that the rest have the intelligence to make their own minds up about what they like or want to do.

Each of the major brewers now had at least one big lager brand name worthy of publicity campaigns, whilst all the regional companies had either their own brand or, more usually, a lager supply deal with one of the majors. Once the voluntary pub swap was over, everyone would be able to see a stable decade ahead; plenty of beer choice and competition, signs of a steady increase in beer sales year-on-year, no reason for large numbers of pub closures (other than those most affected by the drink driving laws), and a new Tory Government that would understand the benefits of the existing successful vertically-integrated structure of the industry. The power of CAMRA to influence public opinion was recognized, but any possible disadvantage to the industry would be compensated by their passionate interest in beer, which could only be good news.

It was with this background of a potentially stable industry, capable of supporting long-term capital investment that I arrived in the west Midlands in 1980, with some 750 pubs and many more 'free trade' outlets with which to cope. My first impression of the area was unfortunate but educative, when I unwisely took a train from Birmingham to Wolverhampton, which revealed what could only be described as a series of vast urban bomb sites of which one could only feel ashamed to be British.

What on earth were foreigners thinking of us when they saw such a complete failure to recover from the war, after 35 years? In fact, the death of heavy industry in the Black Country, the crucible of the Industrial Revolution 200 years before, was already in full swing, and local councils had refused to de-rate any unused industrial building unless the roof was removed! Such a simple but stupid ill-thought-out regulation did nothing to create a desire to regenerate the area; successive governments ignored this rot, subsequently allowing manufacturing industry as a whole to decline over the whole country during the next 20 years.

The central area of my operation was dominated mainly by Bass, resulting from earlier takeovers and mergers of local brewers, plus a successful regional brewer with similar sales volumes, built up over the years from a family business. However this did not exclude many other brewers, big and small, having a good stake in this heavy-drinking area.

*

Before mentioning the word 'monopoly' again, which was to bug the brewing industry from then on, eventually leading to the final destruction of its heritage and strengths at the turn of the millennium, a simple explanation of the structure of this heritage is needed as a reference against the future assaults that it suffered.

In the early 1980s the beer business was fairly equally divided between 'tied' and 'free' trade. The 'tied' trade consisted mainly of brewery-owned tenanted pubs, with the larger houses and hotels managed by company employees. Exceptionally, some pubs would be let on long leases, to self-employed entrepreneurs prepared to invest their own money in the structure of the property. Many off-licence businesses in high streets were also brewery-owned. The restriction on 'tied' tenancies was that all drink sold in the house had to be supplied by the owning company.

The 'free' trade consisted of working men's and similar non-profit making clubs, and all manner of privately-owned pubs, clubs, hotels, shops, restaurants and entertainment venues that had a licence to sell alcoholic drinks for consumption on or off the premises. All these outlets had the opportunity to arrange their own suppliers and negotiate prices in a fully competitive environment.

However, free traders could finance their operations through loans from the local breweries on highly attractive terms, in return for a commitment to buy from them a minimum quantity of alcoholic drink; obviously, the larger the sales of the enterprise the bigger and better the financial deal on offer.

These deals were known as 'tied by loan', and were much criticized because the breweries seemed to be exerting their muscle to 'tie' free trade customers into their products. In fact, such financing was responsible for much higher standards of customer facilities than would otherwise have been the case, and anyway a 'tie' could be cancelled at any time by a competitor offering its own replacement 'tie by loan'.

This system provided the opportunity, particularly for non-profit making members' clubs, to set up and maintain their establishments without impossibly onerous bank loans, whilst being able to sell their drinks at sensible prices. This system was genuinely responsible for the high standards of comfort and quality of these retail outlets *not* owned by the breweries.

However, relatively cheap beer in members' clubs under these arrangements was the biggest bugbear among brewery tenants, who constantly complained about the prices they had to pay and hence charge for their beer, to make a profit. In fact, the difference in retail prices between the two types of outlet simply reflected solely the difference between the normal needs of a profit and a non-profitmaking enterprise.

For all this variety in the beer trade, the tenanted pub remained, at that time, the backbone of the British beer heritage. It was these self-employed landlords, creating their own variety of welcome, service and attractions to their customers, who ensured the continuity of the pub as a centre of a community's social life.

The relationship between the brewery and the tenant was a key factor in supporting the success of this integrated operation. In fact, it was the vertical integration of the whole brewing industry, which extended all the way from the malt and hops through to the presentation of the beer to the customer on the other side of the bar, including the presentation of the pub itself, which ensured quality and price competitiveness.

It was to be the future government-enforced rupture of this particular part of the beer supply chain that was the basic cause of the massive beer price increases of the 1990s, and the subsequent break-up of the whole British brewing industry.

By way of explanation, one can understand that it may be difficult for some people (particularly those who do not like to confuse themselves with too many facts) to see vertical integration as a means of business efficiency for the *benefit* of the consumer; it is equally valid to suspect that such integration can be an opportunity to *exploit* the customer through lack of choice, and to take other advantages of an apparently monopoly position. It is unfortunate that the politicians were to take the latter view and to discover too late that they were wrong.

*

In the early 1980s the industry seemed still to retain some of its traditional paternalism. As a business, the vast majority of the capital employed was in the form of pubs, and most brewing companies were content to earn a modest return on that capital, thus creating a base for sound price competitiveness. They did not see CAMRA's cries of lack of choice in tied outlets as valid; there was barely a pub selling less than four draught beers and a large range of bottled beers, far in excess of almost every other bar in the rest of the world. Neither did they see a serious monopoly situation building up; none of the 'Big 6' exceeded 22 per cent of the whole British market, whilst globally most beer-drinking countries had a brewery with more than

50 per cent, including a few around 90per cent.

The brewery's income from the tenanted estate came from two main sources, the rent and the wholesale profit from the drinks purchased from the brewery by the tenant. Out of this income the property was maintained, and a full delivery and cellar service provided, the latter being the most important requirement for the tenant to be able to serve beer to the highest quality standard. Supplying the cellar and dispense equipment, and the training of tenants to look after cask beer, were key factors in overall customer service and the reputation of the brewery.

The attachment of the tenant to the brewery was further enhanced by the development of personal relationships with the regular delivery draymen, the district manager and the cellar serviceman, all of whom were charged with the same motivation of one single company's fortunes. Such was the strength of this bond in some places that these self-employed tenants felt so company-oriented as to request qualification for the company's employee pension scheme.

The critical factor in stabilizing the future of the whole tenanted estate was the relationship between the rent and the brewery's wholesale profit. Historically, the tenant had paid a 'wet' rent, in other words based on so much per barrel of beer (and an equivalent for other drinks) bought from the brewery. This made it easy for the brewery to set a stable common wholesale price structure per barrel across the whole tenanted estate that ensured sensible retail prices and a sensible brewery profit; but critically, *it allowed the low-sales pubs to survive, where an accountant's analysis of return on capital employed (the value of the pub) pub-by-pub would have suggested instant closure of the lower end of the estate.* These latter houses often consisted of part-time tenancies, the tenant having other employment to keep the wolf from the door, but nevertheless these houses were often among the most important assets of some local communities.

This historical structure of the industry had barely changed by the early 1980s. Beer prices were still at the same equivalent level as in the 1950s, having risen only by the rate of inflation. Rents were now based more on a percentage of tenants' estimated profitability (not all that different from a 'wet' rent).

Inflation was not an important factor in a brewery's finances because, as a rough estimate, on average, a pub was reckoned to be worth the value of its annual turnover. Therefore, the capital assets rose with price inflation at roughly the same rate, thus maintaining the balance of overall return on capital at the moderate levels required for truly competitive pricing.

This moderate level of return was typically 10-11 per cent across the whole industry for several decades. There was no real reason why this state of affairs required any serious modification, and any significant adjustment would surely threaten the existing stability and range of tenanted pubs across the country.

Unfortunately life just isn't like that.

*

Things were beginning to stir. Highly successful tenants earning good money were complaining that they were subsidising the less successful; representations from their National Union of Licensed Victuallers (can you have a union for the self-employed?) were demanding a fairer way of assessing rent, based on *potential* profitability of an 'average' tenant. I explained to the local union representative that since the three most important factors in the success of a pub were the landlord, the landlord and the landlord, an 'average' landlord must be almost indefinable; and even if it was, it would inevitably lead to the demise of the lower end of the estate, where a rent based on 'potential' would be unsustainable.

I met the local union representative.

"Who are you representing when these demands will allow tenants, probably earning four times or more than you, to become even richer, and which will cause the demise of half of your members? And anyway, what are your own ambitions?" I asked him.

"To become a successful tenant," he replied.

Note to file: Try to get to the bottom of someone's personal motives when they claim to be representing others.

As always with negotiations on abstract concepts, the normal compromise was reached, whereby both sides were satisfied that their objectives had been aired to a satisfactory degree; and that the deal, whatever it meant, was acceptable, sort of.

*

At this time, I had also stepped into the latest Monopolies Commission intervention, which had led to the pub-swapping plan among the major brewers as previously mentioned, to reduce domination of pub ownership in certain local areas. This seemed to me to be a relatively simple but time-consuming irritation, until I had to face a deal with another of the 'Big 6' who did not want to swap beer sales. It wanted to swap *rent*.

I had inadvertently discovered why that company's beer, in its few local tenancies, was more expensive than all the others; their brewing operation was a subsidiary of a property-oriented company, with seemingly far more interest in exploiting the value of its properties than its beer, forcing the tenant to recover his high 'commercial' rent through his beer prices. In this way, I became aware of one of the major threats to future beer prices in pubs, should the vertical integration of beer-oriented companies ever be broken up.

*

Note to file: Always keep your eyes open for things of which, if only with the benefit of hindsight, you will, in future, be able truthfully to say 'I told you so'.

At roughly the same time, the tenant 'tie' was being loosened, through the release from compulsion to purchase soft drinks from the brewery owner; this was another minor but significant crack in the system that was protecting the entire tenanted estate in the most efficient (vertically-integrated) format.

One of the unfortunate aspects of vertical integration was the advantage that the tenant could enjoy by concealing part of his trade from the brewery. For example, if he bought a barrel of his brewery's beer from a local cash-and-carry wholesaler with his own money, he could pocket the till takings on 288 pints, thus achieving his gross profit free of any income tax and VAT payments, as well as a potential reduction in rent.

The immediate loss to the Inland Revenue of this 'buying out' was far greater than that to the brewery: I had heard of obvious gross offences being reported to the Revenue, but rarely of them being properly investigated. It was clearly up to the breweries to minimize the scale of this type of activity, presumably prevalent in all cash businesses, in fairness to their honest brethren as much as to preserve the stability of vertical integration.

One particular event occurred that would have been highly amusing if one had been certain that it was not happening to oneself as well. On a certain date in the early1980s the units of volume stated on spirit bottle labels were altered from fluid ounces to centilitres, presumably at the behest of Brussels.

At the time of the change, one of the local breweries happened to have six months' stock of a popular whisky brand in its warehouse, and the management deduced that it would be that length of time before any of their tenants would have 'centilitre' labels of this whisky in their pubs. After three months, all the brewery's district managers were instructed to tour their tenancies and serve notice to quit to any tenant who had a 'centilitre' bottle of that whisky on the optic behind the bar, as incontrovertible evidence of 'buying out', this being a dismissible offence. Inevitably the tenants won the day, due to the impracticability of the brewery getting rid of 75 per cent of them.

Note to file: Think of all the possible ramifications before leaping into disciplinary action for nefarious activities of your people.

I failed in a test of the above-mentioned pearl of wisdom when we decided to give notice to a new tenant who had just transferred from being the manager of one of our managed pubs. After transferring, we discovered that he had been 'ghosting' (inventing non-existent bar staff and pocketing their wages) in his previous job, and we were not prepared to have such a record of blatant dishonesty among our tenants.

The tenant appealed through the normal procedure; this consisted of a tribunal of three representatives for the tenant and three for the brewery, with an independent chairman who had a casting vote. Unexpectedly we lost at the first vote, when the managing director of a brewing company voted against us on the grounds of 'unfairness, if that was all that he was guilty of.'

Were we fighting a losing battle against impossible odds? We thought not, if one accepts the inevitability of a modicum of cash losses in retail outlets, but not of a devious criminal kind. Even then, there was at least one instance of a manager having his case of such dishonesty dismissed by a court, on the grounds that, since his salary was so low, 'what else could the company expect?'

The managers actually had a reasonable total employment package, but it was a hard job for them controlling and being accountable for their staff, many of whom were temporary employees; dishonesty by them, even simply serving free drinks to their friends in the bar, fell totally onto the shoulders of the manager.

However, the state of confusion in the plethora of ways to generate discrepancies in a pub's finances was to be magically solved by a wonderful invention called EPOS (Electronic Point Of Sale). This was the first generation of computerized recording of cash sales and stock control. The expense was enormous, but the suppliers, who said that they knew all about fiddles in retail outlets, had estimated and promised us savings of 2 per cent of turnover: at that rate of return it didn't need an accountant to help us justify the expenditure. What happened, of course, was that EPOS went in (at 50 per cent over budget), and any savings (not many) rapidly disappeared. Also, the fiddles became so sophisticated, to overcome the electronic wizardry, that it became even more difficult to identify and unravel them. Today, of course, 20 years on, electronics have presumably brought all such matters under complete control.

*

Note to file: Don't play with new toys and other things that you don't fully understand. Wait until they are idiot proof.

Trying to maintain the stability of the whole 'tied' estate, managed and tenanted, was only one small part of a business that was forever being watched over closely by the City, as well as the government and other amateur organizations such as CAMRA.

Although the era of the diversified conglomerate was well under way, under the leadership of avaricious ego-tripper entrepreneurs and asset strippers, the early 1980s was when I became aware of the pressure that merchant bankers and brokers were capable of putting on the activities of public companies, and the resulting significant influence that they were having on commercial financial policies. In fact, if one were to attempt a full analysis of the cause of the collapse of the great British brewing heritage, then they would have a pretty fair representation in it all.

As a moderate investor in shares of public companies, I was pleased that we were entering an era of a capitalist style of government, and what turned out to be a golden age of the cult of equity, with the opportunity to create wealth for oneself from the success of all. For this, one needs financial organization at the centre to drive the cult, by providing the investment vehicles suitable for mass involvement (e.g. unit trusts), the force to make companies outperform their peers, and a service to companies and individuals to keep the whole thing rolling (upwards of course).

The first thing that struck me in the early 1980s was the consistency of stock exchange share prices falling whenever reported annual profits did not exceed at least 15 per cent above the previous year. Quite clearly, a cult of 'market expectation' was developing, independently from the realities of company capability to attain such 'targets'. This was reflected in my own operations in two ways. Firstly, and really quite sadly, capital projects were beginning to be refused because they did not give enough return in the short term, although long term they were extremely attractive. Secondly, budgets were beginning to be dictated at levels of sales and profit that one could only describe as speculative, following which any signs of shortfall had to be made up by cutting back (even more than usual) on planned maintenance and other similar overheads.

These sorts of activities can be sustained for a good length of time in a solid well-run company, at least enough to generate an impressive steady record of increases in financial performance. During the 1980s this was helped by a steady small increase in beer consumption in the UK, but industry as a whole was beginning to squeal about short-term attitudes in the City and its possible wilting effect on Margaret Thatcher's capitalism-led property-owning democracy. Equity investors were enjoying a lovely steady rise in the value of their shares, thank you very much.

The second level of expectation in the City seemed to be the need to dilute the risk inherent in large companies having only one speciality product or service. Diversification for such companies that were in a mature market with limited scope for expansion was becoming a much used expression for driving businesses on to greater heights.

One must ask who were the best people to drive and advise

companies on such matters, and to supply the necessary services way beyond the resources and competence of an average company. Answer: the whole of commerce seemed to be having irrevocably to commit itself to the 'expertise' of the City, as financial and legal complexities developed beyond the grasp of company directors, although there must have been practically no-one in the City with experience of actual day-to-day management of a company.

In this way, 'big is beautiful' became a byword: profitable stable companies, unwilling to show such initiative, were being downgraded in the eyes of young MBA graduate analysts who had never set foot in a business. Those companies that had difficulties coping with the expansion or diversification demanded by the City became 'troubled' or 'beleaguered' in the eyes of the press. An unstoppable new concept of what represented successful business had been born, with a new generation of inexperienced but quick-witted theoreticians getting their share of the action and wealth, by driving progress ever harder and ever upwards.

This was seen by many as fair game because the Government was there, in the form of Director of Fair Trading, Monopolies Commission, financial authorities and all other manner of control to oversee fair play. The Big 6 had not escaped the fever, two having already fallen to a hotel firm and a tobacco company; others were making substantial, supposedly synergistic acquisitions in other investment sectors.

*

Note to file:If you have a view on how your world is going, take a note and look again in 20 years to check how accurate you were.

During this period 'in the trade' it was inevitable that one had to come to terms with the local influence of CAMRA. We had good relations locally with an active section enjoying our cask beers as much as those of small brewers. Bass was still the largest producer of cask beer in the world, including Springfield Bitter and Highgate Mild from our small local breweries for the local pubs, as well as widely available regional and national brands: nothing could have been more supportive of the principles of their 'campaign'.

Armed with this range of beers, we started regularly supporting financially the local beer festivals organized by CAMRA, only to be met by abuse from speakers reeling off their political message of the big bad brewers forcing lager and fizzy keg ales down the throats of the beer-drinking public. Keg ales had always tended to have more gas in them, because badly-handled cask beers usually go flat in the cellar, and badly-handled keg beers pick up gas from the top pressure used to dispense them. The policy of Bass was to produce its keg ales with a gas content identical to that of a well-handled cask beer and to install dispensing systems in the pub that minimized any variations in gas levels. This was not necessarily the case with all breweries.

The vindication of this policy arose accidentally, through the pub of ours used by CAMRA for its local monthly meetings. It was chosen by them for its excellent reputation for cask Springfield Bitter, which they had been enjoying for a considerable time. However, it had been forgotten by everyone (other than the publican) that the function room used for their meetings was too far from the cellar to be able to dispense cask beer, and had been permanently fitted up for the keg version!

Being such nice people locally, we decided that discretion was the better part of something or another, and so silence was the order of the day, together with an instruction to continue sponsoring their festivals.

CHAPTER 11

THE BENEFITS OF INFORMATION TECHNOLOGY

The first half of the 1980s was the era of Margaret Thatcher setting up shop after years of government policies sponsored and controlled by the trades unions. In that respect, one of the most important of her missions, as far as industry was concerned, was to establish a proper balance between the rights of employees and the rights and responsibilities of employers, to contribute to the nation's economy through efficient running of their businesses.

Her changes in the employment laws unquestionably allowed companies the scope to manage their businesses as they wanted, with greatly minimised risk of employee problems, but it required a certain element of courage and commitment. Twenty years on, it is sad to see some organizations still firmly in the grip of union power, notably those government-controlled therefore answerable to no one, or those that did not have the will to face confrontation.

Back in the Burton brewery from my temporary detachment, things had been moving well, through 'Peter the Personnel' continuing to keep employee relations ahead of legislation and, surprisingly, the HQ personnel administering some extremely progressive policies. The old attempts in the brewery to crack the barrier and bring a sense of equality between 'them and us' had proved a good start to a major push in that direction throughout the company.

The most interesting aspect of these improvements in working conditions was to observe the reactions of the dyed-in the-wool union officials during the annual negotiations, bearing in mind that an official had union policy to observe, with working conditions greatly inferior to the employees that he represented.One of the great advances towards full industrial democracy was the decision to give an annual issue of Bass shares to all employees, based on company performance. Perhaps it was the mention of the word 'democracy' that inspired the union official to refuse to consider these share issues as part of any working condition package within the gamut of his union. If we wanted to do that, that was up to us.

Our first issue of shares occurred around the time that pioneering Imperial Chemical Industries' first issue to employees came out of the Inland Revenue's compulsory three-year holding period, and thus available to sell if the owner wanted. The media, of course, was full of stories of 90 per cent of the 'workers' rushing to do just that.

The chief of HQ personnel asked me if I thought that we were being sensible to risk that happening to us, thus destroying the purpose of giving employees a feeling of long-term commitment to the company. Knowing that he was an experienced theoretician on personnel matters, and had never made live contact with the shop floor in his relatively short time in Burton, I told him that it was the best thing he had ever done.

I guaranteed him that 90 per cent would hold on to their shares forever and pass these proud symbols of their heritage on to their children and grandchildren. I was wrong. No one could have dreamt then that their proud heritage was to be systematically destroyed in the 1990s, firstly by external influences, then given up and sold by the company, along with the name of Bass, to the Belgians.

A penultimate blow to the local union official was the mention at an annual negotiation of bringing the company private health plan down into negotiated groups of employees. With such privileged 'class' matters being totally against union policy, he blanched and was obviously realizing that this was the end of the line of his influence, apart from strict adherence to haggling over weekly wage rates. That is, until monthly salaries replaced them.

Meanwhile, more progress was being made by equalising pension arrangements for all. With the workforce perceiving a vast improvement in their lot, it was not too difficult to bring sense into buying out old traditional pay discrepancies and restrictive practices in line with a new sense of total involvement in the working of the brewery.

Team briefing was introduced, giving the opportunity to junior managers, some having come up from the shop floor, to solidify identity with company and local events relevant to their teams, and to provide democratic feedback. Abandonment of clocking on in return for handover responsibilities, monthly payments into bank accounts, together with monthly savings plans to purchase Bass shares at (hopefully) knock down prices, all helped to break down further the 'them and us' barriers.

The ultimate achievement of Margaret Thatcher in the 1980s, that settled once and for all these new and better times, was the availability to buy your own council house at a bargain price. The concept of a property-owning democracy was well and truly founded, whereby individuals would transfer their allegiance and energy away from griping to their union about their lot, to the motivation of providing permanent acquisition of assets and quality of life for their families. We knew we were there when one of the most influential union representatives admitted to us that he had just bought his council house, but would we please keep quiet about it!

Gone were the horrible days of long industrial disputes, when resistance was normally supported by the directors, but only until they saw profits seriously threatened.

*

In the mid-1980s, things were changing in other directions as well. In view of the time needed to run a developing complex conglomerate, the chairman's visits were coming to an end, being replaced by annual video presentations of the company's financial results. These HQ contributions to the new democratic policy were invariably as dry as dust, concentrating only on the figures and the subjects that the City (and presumably the directors) were interested in.

The reaction of a substantial minority of our employees, who anyway were sure that profits came as cash in suitcases for the exclusive use of the directors, was 'wonderful, but where is my share of it all?', whilst the rest were more interested in job security than anything else. It was a hard job to convince them that published profits of a company were little more than an indication of tax liability, and what mattered was that they were working for a successful company, through having already used the surplus cash to maintain and expand the business, which is the only way to job security.

*

Note to file: If you want to get a filmed inspirational message across to a wide range of employees, first research what the *audience* wants to hear, and use professional performers.

Information technology was still in early development at this time. Computers had long been used to do obvious simple tasks of number crunching, otherwise requiring huge numbers of people. Examples were analyzing sales data brand by brand, pub by pub, or sending out tens of thousands of bills every week, requiring large whirring machines in remote specialized data processing facilities.

Our first sight of what could be recognized as prototypes of the modern PC had begun to appear on the desks of secretaries to the main board of directors. The first one that I saw working was being operated by Sir's secretary. Sir was on the verge of retirement and was going to run the company's shooting estate: in line with his philosophy of never taking on a job without being fully familiar with all its workings, he had been on a course for gamekeepers. His secretary was typing his notes. I leant over her shoulder to see the wonders of all this coming up, one by one, on her television screen. There, in full view in the centre, was:

The biggest cocks are the most fertile…

Note to file: Use technological aids to keep copious notes on detail, in case you ever have need for a reminder.

The first personal technological advance for the 'doers' was the issue of a car telephone, of a quality appropriate to one's management grade; need did not seem to come into it. One day a man came to tell me that he was to fit a model 3500 in my company car.

When he came back, I was presented with an instruction book too large to fit anywhere handy in my Volvo Estate car, and with a significant part of the car boot filled with expensive looking gadgetry. I discovered from the instructions why it was called model 3500; it had 3500 functions.

After a week, I had figured out how to auto-phone on my way home (to prepare the gin and tonic), and soon I was able to phone anywhere in the company using the normal STD codes, so long as I found a lay-by, got the book out of the boot and spent 15 minutes trying to do it right.

What the man had not told me was that there were actually 3501 functions, having added the facility to auto-dial directly into the company's entire *internal* telephone network. After this discovery and a glorious month of this real hi-tech usefulness, this particular technological wonder facility failed to work any more.

At that moment, I suddenly realized that I was out on my own with only a secretary between me and insanity or, at best, ridicule for being unable to understand or operate a simple piece of essential technology (or even realise that it was essential). I came to be totally dependent on my secretary Annette to see me through these dark days of advancing technology, whilst I thanked God that I had only 2500 working days to go until I retired.

"What do I do about getting this sorted out, Annette?" I asked.

"I think there is a friendly helpline. I'll find out and get it for you."

I speak to Friendly HelpLine (FHL), who sounds worryingly efficient, to tell her that my auto-dialling into the Bass network did not work any more.

"Who's your air time retailer?" FHL demanded. I burst out laughing.

"Why are you laughing, Mr. Ricketts?"

"Sorry, I couldn't help it. Could you explain in words of one syllable what one of those is?"

"An air time retailer is ..er..well..an air time retailer. There is really no other way of putting it," FHL explained, as if it was my fault for not knowing.

"Tell me a bit more if we are going to get anywhere, and I promise not to laugh," I said encouragingly.

"Well," FHL replied, "What paperwork do you get regarding your phone?"

I shouted through the door. "Annette, what paperwork do we get for the phone?"

"Only bills," she shouted back.

"Did you hear that?" I asked FHL. "Only bills."

"Right. What is the name on top of the bills?"

Further shouting back and forth enabled the name of the sender of the bills to be passed on.

"That's your air time retailer." Without pausing to receive my wrath, she sped on. "I have the explanation that you want. We have had strict instructions to prohibit your access to BT chatlines…"

"That opens a whole new can of worms," I interrupted, not knowing what the hell she was talking about. I suddenly decided not to express any more ignorance to her of what might be important high-tech know-how. She continued:

"…unfortunately, cutting off that facility also cuts off the Bass network facility, due to software overlap."

"And why didn't you take the trouble to inform me of this?" I asked with an appropriate balance of politeness, calmness and authoritarian high decibel level.

"Oh, we wait for people to complain," replied FHL.

Note to file: The time comes when you must realize that the next generation must genuinely think it is doing the right things in the right way. And however hard you might try to control this, there is nothing that you can do about it.

The following day I attended a monthly meeting of the trustees of the company pension fund, at which one routine agenda item was to review the cost-saving list of voluntary early retirements; one could always identify a number of splendid excellent colleagues that the company would surely miss. I hoped that they had made the right decision through a combination of the special financial terms on offer, helping the company to execute its cost saving plans, and/or escaping the impending experience of the new generation (an example of which I had suffered the day before).

Later in the meeting the secretary commented on the fact that the number of active (working) members of the pension fund was actually *increasing*, and who were all these people being recruited?

'I could tell you a thing or two,' I *thought*.

*

Pressure on cost cutting in the brewery was as high as anywhere else, particularly as the growth in beer sales was beginning to show a levelling off in the mid 1980s, and the required return on capital from the company's diversification purchase of Holiday Inns seemed to be slow in materializing.

One of the methods for cost saving, of course, was to exploit the rapidly advancing world of information technology; this was perfect for the engineers to pioneer, because if they did not understand its potential, nobody would.

My chief engineer told me that he wanted to install computerised planned maintenance, stock control and other administrative activities in his department. He had approached a computer supplier who could meet our (his) specification for an initial £60,000 that would do enough administrative processing for three clerks to take early retirement. Also, he had three clerks conveniently willing to accept the existing highly attractive, limited-period financial offer, and the computer could be supplied before that deadline.

With this quality of short-term investment (so loved by the company), there was no need to get an accountant to work out the return on capital; it was obvious that we should go ahead immediately with an urgent submission to HQ computer services that controlled these things centrally. Without knowing that the universal desire of ambitious engineers is to be unique and one step in advance of their peers, computer services made the fatal mistake of asking all the chief engineers of the larger Bass breweries around the country if they would like to join in this project.

Their enthusiasm was unbounded, so long as each had computer programmes that suited *their* way of doing things. Unsurprisingly, HQ failed to get any form of agreement among them, thus being forced to dictate the only possible compromise,

193

which was to purchase a commercially available software package (definition of compromise: a solution that suits nobody). By the time the system was delivered the deadline for the three clerks had long gone, as had the clerks. Strangely, the engineers department had seemed to be working perfectly well without them, or the computer. The day the computer arrived, the chief engineer came to tell me that he needed three clerks to operate it.

*

Note to file: Beware IT systems that take twice as much effort to work things out as doing it on the back of an envelope, and then having to do it on the back of an envelope anyway, to check that you got it right.

Note to file: Must remember to explain to the secretary of the pension fund the benefits of IT people in the future of the company.

One of my privileges of working from the Burton brewery was to become involved in VIP visits to HQ. This usually involved giving the visitors a tour of our flagship brewery, then being present at their private lunch with the appropriate main board directors. These were always of great interest by way of learning and observing business dealings and relationships at the highest level of very large companies. For example, I had experienced a sequence of Friday visits from a number of the big merchant banks in London: whether we were courting them or vice versa was not too clear to me.

On the first occasion, the lunch conversation centred on the role of the small shareholder in big business. Bearing in mind that this conversation took place almost 20 years before corporate governance became the 'in' phrase for controlling the behaviour of company directors, the finance director seemed to be well ahead of thought in that direction.

He was expressing concern that small shareholders were

effectively unable to have any influence on the policies and conduct of their companies: all they have is the annual meeting, at which any comment represents minuscule voting power, even if supported by other small shareholders. He therefore expected his financial advisers in the City to play that role on their behalf. This was met by sound commitment by the bankers that this was indeed their philosophy anyway, but I felt a little bit of disquiet.

Here was a City organization that would take tens of millions of pounds in fees to advise, arrange and execute, for example, a takeover of a large company, and if it all went pear-shaped they would take another tens of millions of shareholders' funds to advise, arrange and execute getting rid of it. Surely the temptation of such earnings, through pressurizing companies continually to develop and diversify, far outweigh the rewards extractable from just leaving the company to get on with the things it has always been good at.

Churning this disquiet over in my mind, I suddenly had a vision of a children's playground out in the wild, where the crocodiles had been employed to protect the children from the perils of the jungle. Not fully understanding the rationale of this, I politely kept quiet.

I came away wondering what the City knew about assessing companies' abilities to cope with rapid expansion or other dramatic change. At that particular time, both Bass shares and dividend income (the only measures to the small shareholder) had been performing well, but the recent purchase of Holiday Inns, the first really major diversification away from brewing, at a price that some of the City had seen as rather high, was just starting to show signs of dragging down the overall company performance. But someone in the City must have advised us on a realistic price to pay?

Note to file: Is it true what they say about financial advisers, that they will look after your money until it is all gone?

195

On a further occasion, the lunchtime conversation centred round what made Bass a successful company. If the company still existed I would not, of course, be recording here such sensitive information. Agog with interest, the other bankers and I listened to the finance director coming to an agreement with the head banker that there were two main requirements for Bass to be a successful company – keeping the City happy and borrowing money in the right currency.

Having acquired, as a result of several such lunches, a small degree of confidence amongst such erudite company, I felt that I had to make a contribution, albeit largely through operating mouth before brain.

"That's interesting," I said, "I thought that a successful company is something to do with selling products or services of a quality that customers want to buy, and then to come back time and again for more."

"Very good, Bob," replied the finance director, giving me a look clearly indicating that I had not been invited to these lunches to open my mouth.

Two days later I was summoned to Sir's office.

"Well, Bob," he smiled, "I don't know what you have been saying to the FD and I don't want to know, but he has recommended that you go on a financial appreciation course. So you had better find out which is the best one in the country and go on it."

I ended up on a high-powered course run, quite coincidentally, by the same lecturer who had introduced me to the mysteries of ratios extracted from company accounts as an analytical management tool, during my management course more than 10 years earlier.

I recall one highly relevant event with this professor, from each of these courses. During the first one I had posited in the class that the complexity of company accounts must be such that one figure must surely have to be pulled out of thin air to make the balance sheet balance?

"Only one?" he had replied.

Note to file: Perhaps accounting is a lot more exciting and creative than it seems.

On this second course, obviously at a slightly higher intellectual level, he set a task about a company that had revalued its properties to give a £1 billion surplus, and in the same year had taken over another company, paying £1 billion more than its net asset value. The challenge was: what would be the effect on the balance sheet of that company?

On these sorts of occasions it always seems to be me who has to stand up first and be counted.

"Simply transfer £1 billion from one reserve into another and probably no one will spot the difference?" I suggested as an opening gambit.

"Not a bad answer for someone obviously with no financial accounting experience," replied the professor encouragingly, "but before we discuss the correct answer, is there anyone here who works for Bass?"

"Yes," I piped up, suddenly associating that we had taken over Holiday Inns at the same time as the company had revalued its 8000 pubs.

"In that case it is unfair to analyse to pieces a class member's company in front of others, so we will just discuss the principles involved."

I was left to wonder whether this was the thin end of some wedge, using the profitability of the beer business to conceal the goodwill costs of some huge diversification that might eventually swamp the heritage of the greatest beer company in the country. Ridiculous, of course; despite virtually no synergy between beer and hotels, one had to have faith that we were being led along the path of shareholder prosperity.

*

Going through the second half of the 1980s, the Bass computer services operation was becoming more and more powerful: all the young managers were playing with computers, and all the talk was the development of a paperless society. I found the latter hard to believe; what was going to happen to all the high speed copying and printing machines, and latterly, what does this new expression 'desktop publishing' mean?

With only the limited number of working days that I had left until retirement, I estimated that I might just be able to survive by using 'hard copy' information only, so long as my Annette was there to do the necessary transcriptions from her screen. In fact, quite the opposite from paperlessness happened.

The company reorganized itself into separate subsidiary units and I found myself as a director of the brewing and selling side of the Bass business, entirely separate from the pub operations. Immediately I became swamped with paper; seemingly some of the directors were circulating to all the others every conceivable detail of every single project and its progress, including endless unsummarized routine reports on internal activities.

Regarding my responsibility for all the beer production of the company, I assumed that the other directors were only interested in the beer being supplied of the right quality, in the right volume, at the right time and at the right cost. Thus I found it difficult to compete with the others paperwise, communicating only on need-to-know subjects that affected them.

The main problem of the new job was what to do with all the paper. I calculated that there was insufficient time to read more than half of it, and I noted that about half of the mail came in red folders from the other directors and their minions. So I briefed Annette to transfer all the red folders in the mail into my office cupboard in date order, so that if anyone asked me for comment on one of these circulars, I would be able quickly to find it.

I got no such queries before the cupboard shelves became so distorted by the load that the doors would not close, so I had to instigate a shelf life (no pun intended), rather than risk ostracism by telling the senders not to bother sending their reports.

I was never able to discover exactly why the directors found it necessary to produce and circulate these documents, rather than communicating by exception. My only possible theories were that each director's minions wrote them, to keep *himself* informed of what was going on in his own operation, and/or to impress/confuse the managing director and the other directors with their knowledge, activity and importance.

Note to file: There are better ways of projecting yourself than with showers of bumph.

Another of my VIP responsibilities was conducted tours for the group's non-executive directors when any of them visited Burton HQ for the first time. Invariably they were interesting and challenging people.

The most memorable was at a time when a new management theory was appearing on the market, with a remarkable resemblance to the Management by Objectives of yesteryear. The cycle was returning to base, having delivered wealth and employment to a generation of management consultants.

"What is your mission statement?" he asked me, demonstrating his up-to-date mode.

"I stick to my philosophy of providing beer of the right quality, in the right volume, at the right time and at the right cost," I replied.

"That's your job description, not a mission statement. A mission statement is what you are *inspired* to do next."

"My inspiration is always to do better as the market changes and demands. To me 'right' means the best."

"You must have a specific target like, for instance, to be the most efficient brewery in the country."

"We *are* the most efficient brewery in the country."

"You can't be. Your competitors are boasting in their annual reports about their brewing efficiency, such as figures for process losses of duty paid beer, or barrels of beer produced per employee." The VIP seemed very clued up.

"We passed those figures years ago," I replied.

"So why don't you boast about them in *our* annual report?"

"I don't write the director's report," I said meekly, hoping desperately that he was not going to raise the next obvious question, namely that of my *vision* statement. Perhaps I was a lost cause by then.

*

Note to file: Don't be put off by management-speak gobbledygook, but be inspired by it if you have to.

The end of the1980s represented the time to engage the company succession plan for my impending retirement. Having been consulted by human resources (I cannot recall when the seamless transfer from personnel occurred), I advised them that if the production director was also to direct the scientific and technical resources the replacement would have to be someone who was steeped in the technicalities of brewing, of which an obviously adequate supply of internal candidates existed (plan A).

On the other hand, if the company wanted a manager only (plan B), I told them how essential it was to choose someone who, although necessarily delegating the technicalities, still had the leadership skills to command the resolving of serious technical problems. After all, the art of making beer is to do exactly the same thing day after day until something goes adrift, and to be able to carry the responsibility for leading the resolution of such events. This is the largest part of what a brewing boss should be paid for.

Two years before I retired, human resources were still surprisingly aware of the need for both scientific and technical expertise at the top, so plan A was initiated with a short list of potential candidates for preparation and development for eventual selection. I felt both surprised and happy that human resources were following professional procedures, indeed that they felt it necessary so to do. It seemed to start extremely well. Unfortunately, in times of crisis, things do not work out quite as planned. The crisis in this case came from the Director of Fair Trading launching a full scale monopoly investigation into the brewing industry.

Note to file: Bet your bottom dollar that something will always come along to ruin the best-laid plans of mice and men.

CHAPTER 12

LORD YOUNG STRIKES

1990 was the year of the 'widget', signalling the triumph of technology over the quality of traditional ales. This statement does not apply to Guinness, who had invented this unique procedure to *maximize* the quality of their stout:

Guinness stout in draught form depends on a thick creamy white head as an integral part of the product in the glass, so much so that it had gained a degree of immunity from the law that a pint glass of beer sold had to contain a pint of liquid.

For many years, consistency of this vital characteristic had been achieved by dispensing the beer from the keg under pressure from a mixture of nitrogen and carbon dioxide gases. When dispensed, the release of dissolved nitrogen into the foam stabilizes it, and the reduced amount of carbon dioxide in the gas pressure prevents overfoaming from the beer picking up this gas during storage under pressure in the cellar. These concepts were extended to take-home Guinness in cans by the invention of the 'widget', a small device, gismo, call it what you will, in the can, which releases nitrogen gas into the beer the moment the can is opened, giving the same effect on the beer as previously mentioned.

Perfect head retention or foam stability (identical meanings) on beer had been one of the great unsolved problems when the Brewing Industry Research Foundation opened in 1951. However, despite worldwide research over half a century, no natural process has yet been found of how to ensure a perfect head formation in the glass: hence the intense interest of the ale brewers in this invention, as a possible achievement of what is considered to be a customer's ideal.

Such was the pressure to compete in this latest technology that all manner of widget variations were finding their way into cans of ale. This was despite the knowledge of the brewing scientists that nitrogen gas has an astonishingly flattening effect on beer flavour (one of the reasons that widgets are rarely used in delicately flavoured lagers). Also it is necessary to chill the can prior to opening, if you value your carpets and wallpaper: this lower temperature reduces the strength of flavour still further.

Deaf ears were turned to the observation that only Guinness survives this technique unscathed, through the intensity of its roasted barley flavour and exceptional hop bitterness, which seem to be hardly affected by the use of nitrogen gas. With massive advertising, one or two canned 'widget' ale brands were finding success. This was sufficient to inspire repetition of the Guinness trick on *draught* ales in pubs, and thus was born a whole new genre of 'cream flow' (and similar jargon) ales, culminating in a general reference to 'nitro-keg' beers.

Note to file: When commercial expediency suppresses long term quality considerations, a credible challenge (however pointless) needs to be called from time to time.

The early 1990s was also a time for the appearance on the market of another nascent genre, to become known eventually as 'alcopops'. This was an ingenious invention to produce a beer with virtually no flavour, to which could be added any flavouring that one would normally find in a 'pop', usually fruit-based. The early brand names of these, e.g. Hooper's Hooch, were clearly attracting the younger customer especially. The genre eventually became swamped by similar drinks based on spirits rather than beer, and became so 'popular' that alcopops were reported as displacing beer in the Retail Price Index. At 5 per cent alcohol content, well into the range for premium strength beers, this seems far from an ideal introduction for young people into the benefits of moderate sociable adult consumption.

*

Whether all these developments (so disagreeable to us golden oldies) arose because of, or despite the Monopolies Commission investigation of 1989, is open to debate. However, at the time that the Director of Fair Trading had launched this new threat to the industry, it was difficult to see any justification whatsoever for yet more destructive Government interference.

The brewing industry had barely changed in the previous ten years in terms of beer supply. Bass was still the leader with only 22 per cent of the market, the other big names were still there without any significant concentration or creation of local monopolies, and the range of beers available in pubs far exceeded that of any other country in the world.

Beer was still priced in line with other goods within general inflation. In no real sense of the word was there a monopoly being exploited.

Even CAMRA could hardly complain that a monopoly situation was depriving customers of cask beers. That organisation seemed to be concentrating on encouraging the remaining small brewers of cask beer to retain their independence, and selfishly demanding that (CAMRA's) favourite beers be more widely available in the bigger brewers' pubs.

The historical gripe that brewers were controlling which beers could be sold in their pubs seemed to be an overriding factor in the mind of the Director of Fair Trading, backed by an emotional assumption that this inevitably meant overpricing and lack of choice, as well as disadvantaging the small brewers' opportunity to develop their businesses.

These factors seemed to be a very strange mix for the most conservative of Conservative Governments to want to get involved in, at vast expense to the taxpayer, but so be it. The fault could possibly have lain in parliamentarian apathy by the Conservatives towards an investigation that was initiated by civil servants with strange agendas. Certainly, there seemed to be a strong political atmosphere around the investigation.

The one body to respond to such government interferences was the Brewers Society, which historically had represented every brewery in the country on public and political issues of the day. Equal weight was given to the big and small companies through the widest representation on its council, and it was rare for a policy not to have at least acceptable, if not always universal, support from all the members. However, since the decades of massive concentration, feelings of mutual respect and synergy between the remaining large and small brewery and pub ownerships had developed. This happy, though perhaps slightly complacent arrangement was to be sorely tested.

To cut a long story short, the commission concluded that a 'complex monopoly' existed in the brewing industry. Nobody, except possibly those most closely involved, understood exactly what such a ludicrous oxymoron meant. The only time that I saw 'complex monopoly' in print again during the next decade was a description of the arrangements for medical consultants, when they too were investigated.

I concluded that the 'complex monopoly' in these two cases probably referred to 'potentially unfair exploitation of a limited facility, the size of which is controlled by the government'; in our case the limiting factor was the number of pub licences allowed, and in the medical consultants' case presumably the number of consultant posts available in the National Health Service. However right or wrong this analysis, the medics got away with it (they would, wouldn't they?) and the brewers did not.

Note to file: If you want the easy life, go and work in the public services and be answerable to no-one.

As the commission investigation proceeded, listening to every Tom, Dick and Harry who wanted to see change in the beer trade, the Brewers' Society seemed to adopt a policy of clear, honest, precise analysis and logic in answer to every claim. In every instance the society continually warned the commission what would happen if the traditional vertical integration (from making the beer, all the way through to delivery into the glass at the bar) was interfered with: the price of beer would rocket, the smaller brewers would find it increasingly difficult to survive, leading to further concentration of brewing businesses, and instead of half a dozen major UK-owned brewers there could well be none, and the choice of beers would steadily decline. This would be exactly the opposite of the supposed reasons for launching the monopoly investigation

However, the commission members (with one exception) appeared to take no notice of these representations and accepted more the emotional views of no substance, by opting for a freeing of the market, on the grounds that it would increase competition, reduce beer prices and increase customer choice. The exception in the commission team was one highly intelligent trade union official from the banking sector, who put in a dissenting statement indicating support for the Brewers Society's logical arguments that precisely the opposite would happen.

It was strongly felt that the Brewers Society's arguments were turned down because the commission found it impossible to believe that they were genuine, since the submissions represented both the large *and* the small brewers, and the commission's whole ethos was to 'help' the latter at the expense of the former. So, it came about that the concept of a freer market was published, followed immediately by Lord Young's memorable statement that he was 'minded' to implement all the recommendations, although the insiders knew that he could not conceivably have had time to read the commission's report before spouting about it. Nevertheless, he implemented them, establishing one of the great monuments to the apathy and arrogance of the Conservative Government that eventually led to its downfall.

Note to file: At the risk of being repetitively boring, everyone ought to know that you cannot win a political argument with logic.

The most important of the recommendations, known as the beer orders, that can be used to illustrate best the cause of the subsequent collapse of the brewing industry as we knew it in Britain, were:

1. *Restrictions on brewers owning more than 2000 pubs.* This meant that Bass, with 8000 pubs as one example, had to dispose of half of them. All the big brewers alike would inevitably get rid of the bottom end of their tenanted estates, namely those that had up until then been partly 'subsidized' by the traditional method of fixing rents (*see* chapter 10). These pubs would have to be sold in bulk lots to non-brewers, who would buy them to extract the maximum return on investment in them as property assets, with little concern for, or knowledge of customer service in a pub environment. The luckiest winners here were the City (surprise?) through their massive fees, and the provision of fodder for the scum of the business world, namely the asset strippers. Result: higher beer prices at the bar.

The vertical integration of beer supply was broken, introducing middlemen into the chain, taking their compounded cuts, one on top of the one behind, in the supply chain. Result: even higher prices, and of course increased difficulties in giving efficient service.

The benefits of breweries 'looking after' tenants, by developing long term mutual loyal service and determination to give the best possible beer quality and customer service, was gone. Result: reduced quality of service.

2. *The virtual impossibility of large pub-owning breweries to expand production or pub ownership in the future.* This was to cause the large breweries to review the whole position of owning pubs (or breweries) at all. Most of the benefits of operating an efficient vertically integrated business were destroyed anyway, thus causing a growing interest in specialization in one or the other, or even neither.

This specialization indirectly affected the ability of small brewers to expand beer sales as intended by the commission. The pubs retained by the big brewers were inevitably those generating the most profit: they tend be of the well-advertised 'theme' variety, selling only well-advertised popular beer brands and food, virtually excluding access to the smaller brewer.

3. *Availability of 'guest' beers in tied pubs.* Although the requirement to expand the choice of beers offered in pubs was all with the best of intentions, it involved a further break in the efficiency of supply and hence contributed to the overall distaste of the large brewers towards tenanted estates. Such guest beers are common today, but the expense of transport from and then back to a remote brewery, combined with the age of the beer when it gets to the pub, does not always do a lot for the reputation and profits of the supplier.

Certainly the scale of this facility today could hardly be meeting commission expectations. I find a guest cask beer in a local pub of too variable a quality to take seriously, but I once asked one of the bigwigs of CAMRA what the excitement is of a cask beer served with fish guts and seaweed (clarifying agents) floating in the cask, compared to a bright sparkling keg beer. He replied that the excitement is not knowing whether you are going to get a decent pint or not!

Note to file: Try thanking God that there are people out in the wide world that make life such an interesting pastime for us ordinary mortals.

In reviewing the full horror of what had happened, it is beyond belief that a *Conservative* government could deprive traditional businesses of their right to employ their capital assets as they wish, and could do it in such an arrogant and arbitrary manner without proper consideration of the arguments. The only conclusion that I could draw was that there must have been a long-term lack of rapport between the Brewers' Society and the ruling politicians, and so a part of the blame could perhaps lie with the former?

*

It is difficult to record all the interrelated factors that led to the failure of the smaller brewers to be able to take full advantage of this so-called fantastic freedom and opportunity for expansion provided by the government. What actually happened to one particular company might serve as an illustration of the validity of the Brewers Society's arguments:

Wolverhampton & Dudley Breweries was (and is) a regional brewing company with a high market share of pubs and beer volume in the west Midlands, with well-established popular regional brands. Because of its medium size, the company had been immune from the latest, and indeed any previous government investigations involving monopolies.

On this occasion it seemed openly to disassociate itself from the Brewers Society's reactions to the beer orders, presumably appreciating the potential access to *all* the pubs in its region, whether in the large brewers' pubs as guest beers, or sale of beer to those pubs forced to be sold, or even possibly to buy some of these pubs as they were forced cheaply onto the market. There was also the potential for increased distribution of their brands to the freer market outside the region. Quite right too, and good luck to them, even if it made a nonsense of the government plan for *increased* variety in local concentrations of pubs. If any medium-sized brewer could make a success of all this, there were none better placed than Wolverhampton & Dudley.

Several years later the company fell off the bottom of its Stock Exchange FTSE 250 index of the country's top medium-sized companies, as a result of declining share price due to mediocre performance. The company then decided that the only way forward was to expand by acquisition of other small brewers in the region. Apart from an acquisition in Hartlepool some distance from its heartland, it took over Mansfield Brewery, and Marston's in Burton, with the company stating that being big was the only way forward in the beer orders environment! Thus disappeared three more independent brewers into the hands of a still 'immune' middle-sized group, enabling it to return to the FTSE 250 index.

Other smaller brewers with share quotations experienced similar difficulties during the 1990s, but have mostly survived as independents, but with little organic growth. In fact, some of the most successful ones have been those with the courage and resources to market their one most special brand not only in UK but internationally as well. One or two others got burnt fingers on attempted diversifications (with City advice and appropriate fees presumably). Similar to Wolverhampton & Dudley, Greene King has absorbed some of the great beer names from other small brewers in their region of eastern England. They have now had to face the wrath of CAMRA for closing 'heritage' breweries and moving the brewing to other, more modern plants.

It is strange that these remaining medium and smaller brewers are sometimes referred to in the financial press as 'specialist' brewers. How ignorant can the outside world be? They are the only *generalist* brewers left, still performing most adequately as traditional vertically-integrated brewers; but none have been able to achieve anything like the benefits that the commission promised to provide as justification for turning the industry upside down.

In the light of the worries of many smaller brewers in the new environment, they realised that the Brewers' Society was no longer able to represent their interests and therefore created a separate group exclusively for their needs. The society itself was being pressurized by the supermarkets, as major retailers in the growing take-home market, by demanding an equal involvement in dealing with political and public issues regarding beer.

The society took the supermarkets in, changed its name and has subsequently changed its name again to try to adapt to whatever the needs are today for them. With the destruction of the industry structure that they had represented, perhaps they will have a whole new influence on the consistent all-pervading modern threat - Brussels.

*

The fate of the thousands of pubs that the beer orders released on to the market from the big brewers illustrates again the futility of the 'winning' arguments. A whole mixture of investors came out of the woodwork, ranging from banks and venture capitalists, through small entrepreneurs and asset strippers aiming for the big time and with no pub experience. Some experienced pub operators have entered the fray, aiming to become successful owners of large chains, using all the professional aspects of that business. Unfortunately they seem to be much in the minority.

The net result was initial intense activity to take financial advantage of all the undervalued pub property, followed by squeezing the maximum possible value out of the assets as going concerns, followed today by the trading of pubs in huge blocks to others who think that there is yet more squeezing potential in them.

Within 15 years of the orders, the pubs are now in as much a 'complex monopoly' situation as the brewers were at the time of the commission investigation: but they are in the hands of different people, with tenants now being charged property-based rents, many still tied to their owners for their selection of beers, and often being charged extortionate wholesale prices.

Therein lies the main explanation for the doubling in real terms of beer prices at the bar (*see* Chapter 1) during the 1990s, and thus probably for the declining beer market during that period. Never mind, all the new middlemen and, of course, the City must be laughing all the way to the bank.

*

All of the large breweries, of course, went through their own turmoil in the 1990s after losing most of their pubs. The concept of vertical integration on the large scale had been destroyed, and decisions had to be made whether to carry on as best as one could, specialize in either brewing or pub ownership, and/ or diversify.

The vultures were out too in this brewing arena in the form of foreign brewers, waiting for the chance to move into the supposedly much freer market. They showed little interest in pub ownership, presumably due to the incomprehensibility (to a foreigner) of the traditional British way of running them, to which must be added the government's own level of incomprehension of the whole pub scenario. So, starting with the Big 6 at the start of the 1990s in a complex monopoly, ten years or so later we have a Big 5, presumably *not* in a complex monopoly, of which only one is British – Scottish & Newcastle.

*

Note to file: If the British cannot run a British brewing industry, what is it about foreigners that makes them think that *they* can? And they can. Surely it must have something to do with them not having to respond to the rigours, rules, influence, pressure and sometimes idiotic expectations of the British Stock Exchange and City?

The fate of Bass is probably the saddest of all the horrors that the industry faced in the ten years or so following the Lord Young edict.

By 1990, Bass had got rid of most of its best-forgotten diversifications of the past, apart from hotels. Since the acquisition of Holiday Inns, criticized by the City at the time for paying too much for them, the hotel business had reached a critical mass, therefore able to be assessed in its own right alongside the beer operations. Synergy between the two operations barely existed.

Pressure was on for the company to perform in the light of the stagnating effect of the beer orders. The Bass beer business was clearly permanently limited by decree to organic growth through free trade beer sales, and custom in its remaining pubs. Successful as this might have been, it would not be enough to meet future City expectations. It was inevitable that future hotel acquisitions (no longer diversification, of course) were more likely to satisfy the City: whether the shareholders would be satisfied was another matter.

In what may have been seen by some as a last ditch stand, the managing director of the brewing and sales division was replaced by someone with a completely different outlook on life. He had been trained internally with Bass HQ thinking and with little or no direct experience in handling large operations, large numbers of people and critical profit centres.He clearly had a *carte blanche* to do anything to raise profit expectations in what was now forecast to be a long-term declining beer market. The only real potential was substantially increased market share, something Bass (and most other brewers) had not achieved in living memory.

In hindsight it is fair to say that this type of situation was so impossible that it could only be tackled in one way – bring in management consultants to advise, and to dilute the excuse in the event of failure: quite enough reason in anyone's book to spend several million pounds of shareholders' money. Thus, I enjoyed becoming involved for the first time with one of the top world-wide management consultancy firms; I say 'enjoy' because it was only months before I retired, and therefore I was also able to be filled with gratitude that the experience would never be repeated.

There was little that we did not experience about the latest theories of dynamic management as the consultants guided the directors through the process of 'facilitating' our efforts to resolve our ambitions. This instantly raised serious questions about the ability of these bright young things fresh from business school, brainwashed by their seniors into their consultancy 'formula', being able to lead us into *practical* solutions. As the consultancy developed, such future commercial tactics drifted into the distance under the wealth of theory, MBA-style analysis and dissection, and the total absence of practical advice. For some time I had felt an urge to get to the bottom of what I 'knew' management consultants were capable of contributing to businesses; eventually I was able to get one in a corner to put my question:

"Please tell me, bearing in mind that top management consultants are usually called in only when one has no idea what to do next, and that your huge international experience must have tackled numerous similar commercial problems, why not cut through all the erudite analysis we are going through and talk about practical solutions, taken from the experiences of others in the past? Discussing known practical techniques and their successes and failures could then allow us to focus all your theory into a real-world scenario applicable to us."

"We are not allowed to talk about other clients' problems", was the reply.

"Not even anonymously?" I asked, stupidly.

"Not even anonymously." Q.E.D.

Several million pounds later, Bass launched a strategy of 'controlled aggression' into segments and regions of the beer market. The day that one of our smooth slick salesmen sold our premium flagship Draught Bass into a selected area at a huge 'commodity' discount, I knew finally that our great heritage was permanently doomed.

A further strategy, of empowerment and appropriate bonus reward to all employees, was theoretically an excellent move forward. Unfortunately, as with any modern management development, it only works if the directors are totally clued up and committed to its success. Despite all the grooming undertaken by the consultants to raise comprehension of managerial behaviour towards empowered employees, it all went sour when someone was reprimanded for an expenditure he initiated to save a commercial crisis. The profitable cost/benefit ratio had been obvious. He was told by one of the senior directors that he was only empowered to *save* money, not to spend it.

*

I was walking past the open door of the director of human resources, when I overheard the new MD:

"Andy, when Bob Ricketts retires I want to replace him with a s***…….."

Catching no more of the conversation, my first reaction was 'bang goes all the effort and years of development of the short list for my replacement', that had been supported by the previous MD *and* this director of human resources: certainly, in my eyes, none of that short list fitted the new required specification.

There was, of course, always the possibility that he was simply seeking a seamless progression in the job - accurate self-assessment never was my strongest point. I wondered how my fellow directors, particularly those too young to draw a pension, were feeling after the onslaught of the consultants and their obvious confidential interchanges with the MD: it was beginning to look to me as though a complete clear out might be on the agenda.

Note to file: Perhaps it is part of nature that as you advance towards a major lifestyle change like retirement, circumstances *automatically* arise that make you look forward to it.

It so happened that the MD chose Plan B, replacing me with *two* new directors, so I never discovered which (or both?) met that specification that I should not have overheard.

EPILOGUE

The day that I retired in 1992, the main effects of the Monopolies Commission had not yet fully manifested themselves. Pub disposals had already started; it seemed that Japanese banks were in the lead for grabbing large holdings. The Brewers' Society had been right.

There were six big brewers of the beer still there: Bass, Allied breweries, Scottish & Newcastle, Courage, Whitbread and Guinness. A decade later there were five:Scottish & Newcastle (who had absorbed Courage), Interbrew (Belgian, who absorbed Whitbread's and Bass' brewing), Coors (American, who absorbed half of Bass' brands and breweries from Interbrew), Carlsberg Tetley (Danish, who absorbed Allied's brands) and Diageo (Guinness, merged into this huge wines & spirits conglomerate). Hardly any of them now own any pubs at all and there is only one British major brewer, becoming increasingly international. The society had been right.

The pubs that came on the market, virtually all of them in the last decade, are still being traded by a whole range of interests – banks; venture capitalists; entrepreneurs and asset strippers with no experience in pubs; smaller brewers; experienced pub chain managers trying their hands at ownership (all too few); Uncle Tom Cobley and all. The society had been right.

The new pub chains are now in a very similar 'complex monopoly' position as the brewers were a decade ago. The society had been right.

The price of beer doubled in real terms during the 1990s, and is still increasing above the rate of inflation. This has been due to the increase in middlemen since the break-up of vertical integration, and the entrepreneurial way of charging the highest possible open-market rent to pub tenants. An approximate allocation of the excessive price rise, between property and management considerations, can be arrived at by comparing the 'no frills' managed pub chain of Wetherspoons charging around £1.50 per pint, against more than £2 per pint in a typical tenancy, and £1 per pint that beer would have been priced by the big brewers, had their system not been broken up, and price rises kept within rates of inflation.

An equally confirmatory proof of this retail pricing disaster is that, ten years ago, mild surprise was continually expressed that it was possible to buy beer in cans in a supermarket for a little less than the retail draught beer equivalent in a pub, despite the high cost of canning and packaging beer. Today it is possible to find in supermarkets some beers being promoted at *one third* of the equivalent pub retail price; and these will surely not be loss leaders. The society had been right.

*

By the mid-1990s, Bass had moved from being the best to the worst company for brewers in which to learn their trade, according to a straw poll held occasionally by members of the Institute of Brewing, the body that controls professional qualifications in brewing. Threats by Bass to sell its brewing business if it did not perform to the requirements of the company and the City (assumed to be identical) were becoming more and more real. A decision was made to break its own vertical integration to its remaining customers, by contracting out beer distribution to a joint venture with a logistics giant; this hardly helped motivation to survive. The City probably appreciated it.

Patience presumably ran out, concomitant with increasing complaints about the mediocre progression of the Bass share price and profit performance; Bass Brewers (the brewing and sales division) *was* put up for sale. Since the government would almost certainly not allow a 22 per cent market share to be acquired by another of the big British brewers, it was more or less inevitable that it would be a new foreign acquisition. An unconditional sale to Interbrew, the Belgians already in the Big 6 with their Whitbread beers, at a price considered generous, was achieved. This led to the shreds of the Bass heritage becoming a political football yet again.

Interbrew was then forced by the government (on monopoly grounds) to sell on a major part of its Bass brewing empire, leaving them with only the Bass brand name and those in Scotland and Northern Ireland, where Interbrew had low market share This meant that the new owners of the Bass heritage had no use for the Bass brewery in Burton, and so no proper home for Bass beers. Interbrew sold Bass' Carling and Worthington brands plus the spare brewing facilities (including Burton), as commanded by the politicians, to Coors of Colorado.

Within this shambles, Coors had to inherit also the wonderful Bass Museum of Brewing History on the Burton brewery site, but neither the name nor the Bass artefacts within! As I write this epilogue, a last chance hopefully exists for this, the only world class brewing heritage site in existence, to be saved in its entirety. Thanks to the government, this task is now left for Belgium and the USA to sort out.

No-one should be surprised at the neglect by Bass for this heritage during the melee of disposals; the only time that I knew of my chairman to have toured the museum, his sole memorable question was to know the knacker's yard value of a dead shire horse.

After all the enforced break-ups of the company, Bass was left with a hotel business, and the cream of the pubs and restaurants that the government had previously allowed the company to keep. These two businesses were demerged, at a cost to the shareholders of £80 million in City charges/fees.

The new pub company, renamed Mitchells and Butlers, then was more or less forced by circumstances to 'securitize' their pubs; this is a piece of financial juggling that makes it far less attractive for asset strippers, or others more interested in the properties than the beer business, to attempt acquisition. Result: yet more business for the City, and yet another middleman to take his cut. The Brewers' Society had been right.

The real sorrow from this financial jungle should be for the generations of Burtonians, and indeed those from other traditional brewing towns, who gave their loyal all to the great brewing heritage. In particular are those Bass employees so proud to have received and bought shares in the company as a result of their own efforts, thus creating a tangible part of their personal heritage to pass on to future generations.

All they have now are a smaller number of shares in an international hotel company and a pub company, neither with any allegiance to any particular beer brands. After all these changes, the total current value of these shares, including past dividends and payouts, add up to an investment that would have been far better employed in a building society for the last 10 years or more. Some may have preferred this wealth under the mattress. Never mind, the City has had a ball.

As the pub world settles down in its *new* complex monopoly scenario, new problems start to arise that need to be dealt with. The most serious is the rapid development of binge drinking among the young, supposedly through the entirely unsuitable alcopops and discounting tactics, occurring mostly in high-rent pubs that have to have high-volume throughputs to survive.

Under these conditions, pub tenants are necessarily being forced to turn a blind eye to their social responsibilities associated with pub disciplines, which were second nature to the traditional brewers. New priorities in the police force seem to have reduced the old monitoring of publicans' handling of excessive drinking, placing the blame back on to the pub owners. One may well ask how a Japanese bank would handle that responsibility?

From 2005, the control of licences to sell alcohol passed to local authority responsibility. Thus has died the last vestige of a hugely successful, largely self-controlled national culture and heritage that gave us many decades of social pleasure and cohesion by providing good, cheap beer in agreeable surroundings to every locality in the land.

Note to File: Who was it who first said 'No situation is so dire that government interference cannot make it worse'?

APPENDIX

FILE OF USEFUL THINGS TO REMEMBER

Chapter 1

When faced with a deliberately degrading insult from your superior:
1. Look him straight in the eye.
2. Adopt a facial expression half way between a total blank and mild incredulity.
3. On no account operate mouth before brain.
4. Obtain any required relief by writing obscene messages on the roof of your mouth with your tongue.

It must be a good idea to have a stock of useful phrases that say 'Yes', meaning 'No'. Or, at best, to be able to say both 'Yes' and 'No' without contradicting yourself. If you have any doubts about this ability, just think of your MP.

The vultures are everywhere. Even among those who must project intellectual honesty as an essential prerequisite to their work.

In the field of discovery, it doesn't matter if you are *second*, so long as you are *right*! Synonym: always include some 'Me Too' research in your armoury of commercial research and development projects. If you have any doubts about the value of this, just think of Bill Gates.

Always judge people, organisations, even nations by their actions, not their words. If you have any doubts about this, just think of the world's worst dictators.

To command respect from your underlings, you must keep up with modern terminology and jargon. If you have any doubts about this, just think of some of our judges.

Success in business is all about individuality and commitment, but make sure first that it is not going to kill you.

It seems to be a good idea to know what you are doing before you do it.

Think of life as one long process of picking up pearls of wisdom.

Beware the possible effects of others' senses of humour on your own prospects. And your own for that matter.

It pays to know your place in the family hierarchy.

To succeed in business you must obviously have the right relationship with accountants. Or is it true that *every* accountant is a condom on the spearhead of progress?

Chapter 2

Always keep yourself and your employees up to date with the latest management tools.

The secret of commanding respect from others is to be seen to respect their territory, with due humility towards their own skills and ways of doing things, in exactly the same way that you will expect this from them.

In positions of high authority, style is all important.

A sharp tongue or hard outer crust, on someone who is in a position of power, is nothing to fear. They all have a soft heart underneath; the key is to know how to get to it. Rather like a cactus or a pineapple, I suppose.

There really is nothing new under the sun, absolutely nothing if you go back far enough. It is just bad luck if you happen to have been born in the wrong time warp.

Don't believe everything that your boss tells you. He often has other agendas to take into account at the same time, most probably of a self-preservation nature. Are all bosses like this?

To advance yourself in the eyes of your employer, being in the right place at the right time, and the ability to cover a hole that you dug yourself, are probably more important than any other strategy.

An ounce of image may be worth a pound of performance, but don't press your luck *too* far.

There are always limits to what you can be expected to tolerate. But don't expect your boss to take any notice of them.

When you know that you are not in the same league, it is better to admit it rather than trust to luck that you will not be found out.

Some people can get away with anything. Be envious, rather than try to imitate it yourself.

Beware of large jolly drivers in large purple cars.

There's more to managing people than meets the eye. Or, for that matter, any other part of the anatomy that might get in the way of irate workers.

Chapter 3

The battle for human rights among the downtrodden workers clearly needs to go far beyond getting attitudes right in their workplace alone.

There is nothing like effective advanced planning.

Discretion is the better part of quite a lot of other important things. It seems to be quite a useful management tool.

There is no limit to the degree of commitment that you can give in support of the products for which you are responsible.

Autonomous revenue-raising bodies answerable to no-one are like elephants. Not only do they have long memories, you have to do everything to avoid them either treading on you, or charging at you, or heavily defecating upon you from a great height.

There is always an identifiable system in any madness.

Never give a direct 'No' to an unreasonable request, particularly when you need to develop the enquirer's co-operation. To keep them hanging on in hope, have a battery of responses appropriate to the occasion, which might range from 'Definitely maybe' to 'I'll put it in year 4 of my 3-year plan'.

There is more than one way of getting satisfaction from becoming involved with pigs.

Always put your customers first. Even if you, yourself, have to go without.

Always keep your options open on your work plans. But not too obviously. Meanwhile, try not to behave routinely as if the day has started without you.

By all means develop your wider talents yourself, but don't expect your existing employer to take any notice of them. Particularly if your latest acquired skill would outclass your boss.

If you need a modern-day Jeeves to complete your front line Company presence, they are not as difficult to find as you might think. Look further down the hierarchy.

Be sympathetic towards highly disciplined but outdated management controls; it is the fact that a strong discipline exists which is the most important. The controls can then be worked on at an appropriate time and speed.

Chapter 4

Effective contribution of a service function towards solving problems is entirely dependent on the respect that that function commands. This includes, most importantly, its ability to preserve the dignity of the user.

There is nothing like keeping up with technological advance, and exploring its domestic potential before it ever reaches the home.

In many respects, it is *men* who have been struggling for equality since the dawn of time.

Company loyalty has many facets, both beneficial and rather

less so. In a paternalistic environment, one is rewarded by job satisfaction, security and the chance of at least slightly eccentric enjoyment. Adversely, be prepared for a certain meanness of spirit from above: this is not intentional, but as a result of little knowledge of how the other 99.9% live. On balance, it's not a bad existence.

The time usually comes to every man, at some time or another, to consider surrender. But not when you are having your brains bashed out against a brick wall.

It is a good idea to review the effectiveness of your resources from time to time, and to reallocate them accordingly.

You must have the confidence to stand up to overwhelming threats and disbelief of your competence in high places.

It is surprising how often a technological advance seems to occur which fulfils a long unfelt need. Only to discover that you do actually need it.

There is nothing like keeping your people on their toes.

Consultants obviously have a place in the world, to help those who ought to know better.

Leave nothing to chance when you know that your reputation might be at risk.

Always be wary of putting yourself into any situation where you might have to activate mouth before brain. Particularly after you got away with it the first time.

There are many ways to skin a cat. Including those that you would never think of in 100 years.

In 90% of cases, promotions are as a result of being accidentally in the right place at the right time. The other 10% is reserved for those with the skill to *get* themselves into the right place at the right time.

Chapter 5

Consider ISO 9000 as a good example of the triumph of bureaucracy over natural good management practice.

The best way of selling an idea is not to sell it but to get the receiver to want to buy. Put another way, get the receiver of an idea to believe that he thought of it first.

Paternal chucking into the deep end seems a good way of achieving a new discipline, style and culture. However, for the fastest results, the chucker-in needs to be close, involved and committed. And big.

Confirmation received that Monday *is* a great day for changing a Company's culture.

Adaptability in dress for all occasions is a vital factor in creating a good impression and influencing people.

If all competitors receive the same rate of discount, in perpetuity, then logical analysis must conclude that no way can it be a discount at all. If you have any doubts about this, think it through. Crafty buggers, these civil servants.

Do not confuse information with knowledge. It becomes knowledge when you know what to do with it, and then *want* to do it. And only when you have done it, does it become know-how.

The contents and tools of management information seldom reflect the importance indicated by their heading or title. But if they are any good, one day they will. For instance, how many decades did it take for word processors to be able to process words?

One must always try to find out what is the right thing to do with what others think is essential information. Meanwhile, carry on doing what *you* think is right.

There is nothing like a little bit of ambition in your psyche. But be careful how you show it.

When cloistered with a bunch of inferior equals, reward yourself and your Company by flying its flag as hard as you can.

Beware management techniques that have undergone so much change and development that they have arrived back at the starting gate.

It is said by some that the ideal form of government is a democratic dictatorship. Perhaps this idea comes from industry, where it appears that the nicer the manager running a one-man committee, the better the results.

There really is something going for this psychometric testing business.

Making one's efforts a priority must be a key managerial function, in order to concentrate on the most important things of the moment. But with the arrival of the science of Time Management, will everyone be spending their time planning it?

Chapter 6

When thrown into the deep end by your predecessor, don't panic. The chances are that the operation is so well delgated that it has been running perfectly well without him.

Think twice before referring to *all* accountants as mysterious, or any other adjective that might imply devious creativity. Some seem to be disarmingly straightforward and honest.

In most circumstances, you can fool all of the people some of the time; but to be really clever, just fool the right people all the time. But where is the long-term satisfaction in that?

You may be able to take a horse to water and make it drink, but it is a lot more difficult to take a dinosaur and make it think. But do maintain good personal relations with the accountants. It won't necessarily do the operation much good, but some of them are actually quite fun. Particularly at their leaving parties.

Always try to involve your service functions in a feeling of collective involvement and responsibility for the success of the operation. It might happen one day.

It is useless to think that giving in to ludicrous demands will resolve an issue. There are always endless supplies of new, even more ludicrous ones.

Beware talking openly of any management action that you might or might not want to make use of in the future. Whichever way, you will surely be out-manoeuvred. This is because open honest management (which we all like to think we practice?) stands little chance against animal cunning.

Never underestimate the role of trades unions and the City in leaving Britain behind in the economic progress of post-war Europe.

It is always better to assume that your personnel department will cock things up. It makes it that much more agreeable on the occasions when it doesn't.

Be ever aware of alternative profitable uses for your Company's equipment.

Learn a lot about life from how available resources are prioritized by others.

Stop being nasty about accountants. They probably can't help it.

What is it that they say about one law for the few, and one for us? Clearly, different needs require different rules.

If you know that you are going to upset a personnel director, it is better if he is not yours.

Always explore the wisdom of elders, no matter how bizarre or potentially unfruitful the prospect. You will always find a pearl.

Things can quite suddenly turn surreal, with no warning. When they do, be prepared for a wave of totally unpredictable bizarre events.

Be careful how much you support so-called 'progress'. It may be at the expense of a social structure that is of greater value than that of your strategic goal.

Always include local history in the equation of your business tactics. You will never forecast accurately any reaction, but afterwards you will be able to prove that you did your best. But expect your boss to remark 'Pity it wasn't good enough'.

Crises, when remote from immediate help, require balanced judgment, decisiveness, not a little psychology, and the ability to filter back the right information to your distant superiors on a need-to-know basis. This will invariably be analyzed with the benefit of both factlessness and hindsight, so expect all your decisions to prove to have been totally wrong.

There can be many reasons for unusually high demand for 'consumable stores' in a research department. But it will usually be well targeted. And give beneficial results.

Never be discouraged by a customer reaction that you would have preferred not to have heard. You can always explain it away as the exception that proves the rule. Once.

Chapter 7

Restraint in difficult circumstances is a great virtue.

Always be aware of the diversity of priorities amongst your seniors, and be prepared to honour them.

In my book, Sod's Law is 'If anything can go wrong, it will', and Murphy's Law is 'If nothing can go wrong, it still will'. But in most cases, it doesn't really seem to matter which is which.

It is important to learn and adapt to a Company's procedures for justifying capital expenditure.

Always have some options available when you have the courage to speak your mind to your masters.

Do not underestimate the power of the consumer to be able to reject a new product purely because of its name.

There are many ways of creating a favourable, disciplined environment in the workplace.

Look after the pennies and the pounds will look after themselves. Or something like that.

Broadening your knowledge of others' ways of life helps you to become more certain of your own.

Chapter 8

There come times in everyone's life when an act of duplicity, if not hypocrisy, becomes unavoidable. Rather than try to talk your way out of it, as any politician would do, it is far better and more comforting to be completely honest and have a good laugh about it.

Never deal with a political issue by the use of logic, but it is essential to find out *what* technique to use. Perhaps God (or consultants) will let us know one day.

Wonderful new packages for making us better managers are easily sold to those bosses (and HQs) who can't provide the necessary inspiration or expertise themselves. There is therefore a huge competitive market for consultant-designed techniques, with concomitant short shelf lives. This lets the bosses feel continually up-to-date and 'with it', keeps consultants in profitable employment, and leaves you pretty well free to go on being ..well.. you.

There are ways and means of educating excessive officialdom and getting away with it. But be selective in your choice of technique, dependent on your personal skills.

The next time you come up against an ignorant, aggressive little tin god trying to dictate the way you run your life, just bear in mind that if there was a world war on he/she wouldn't be there. And surely this is better than a war?

Always open a long-term strategy with an impossibly 'ideal' objective, but which illustrates the essence of what might become possible.

Stand by to be surprised when you start something like true consultation, but never show it.

There is nothing better than keeping accountants in useful employment by giving them an insoluble challenge to ponder over.

Confirmation received that accountants *are* condoms on the spearhead of progress.

When you have a charismatic leader as your boss, you get to know pretty well exactly where you are with him.

Respect, understanding and interest for people on their own territory gives the best chance of gaining respect in return.

It never pays to try to correct a professional who has been trained (or brainwashed) into drawing dogmatic textbook conclusions about people's health.

There is only one person in the world to decide what is good for you. You.

Chapter 9

Important high-level decisions, involving several sections of a business. are best arrived at through consultation down to the 'doer' level. This never happens. At least until it is too late.

Times come when you need to recognise when to stop bashing your head against a brick wall, but you must still go on behaving like a gentleman. It is surprising how quickly things can resolve themselves if the other side is left to find out for itself the stubbornness of its ways. (In this case they didn't – perhaps this doesn't work with foreigners).

Resolution: I must stop making notes about accountants. Are they all the same, all the time?

Left-wing politics and fanaticism seem to go hand-in-hand. You need to worry even more if intellectuals are involved as well. And what to expect if they come from Hammersmith as well?

Have you noticed how often directors exempt themselves from the wonderful schemes that they have ordered for improving the efficiency of the Company?

Must find out why royalty seem to be surrounded by an impermeable barrier of establishment hangers-on and formality, of no significance in the modern world. Perhaps it is the hangers-on who have the vested interest in maintaining *their* pretence of superiority and remoteness from the common herd.

Forget the old paternalistic ignorance of how others live. Modern top management is just as bad.

Be grateful for all the helpful bits of advice you get from on high.

Keep your eyes and ears open all the time as to where you really are within the hierarchy.

Chapter 10

Always remember that fanatics cannot accept that the rest have the intelligence to make their own minds up about what they like or want to do.

Try to get to the bottom of someone's personal motives when they claim to be representing others.

Always keep your eyes open for things of which, if only with the benefit of hindsight, you will, in future, be able truthfully to say 'I told you so'.

Think of all the possible ramifications before leaping into disciplinary action for nefarious activities of your people.

Don't play with new toys and other things that you don't fully understand. Wait until they are idiot proof.

If you have a view on how your world is going, take a note and look again in 20 years time to check how accurate you were.

Chapter 11

If you want to get a filmed inspirational message across to a wide range of employees, first research what the *audience* wants to hear, and use professional performers.

Use technological aids to keep copious notes on detail, in case you ever have need for a reminder.

The time comes when you must realise that the next generation must genuinely think it is doing the right things in the right way. And however hard you might try to control this, there is nothing that you can do about it.

Beware IT systems that take twice as much effort to work things out as doing it on the back of an envelope, and then having to do it on the back of an envelope anyway, to check that you got it right.

Must remember to explain to the Secretary of the Pension Fund the benefits of IT people in the future of the Company.

Is it true what they say about financial advisers, that they will look after your money until it is all gone?

Perhaps accounting is a lot more exciting and creative than it seems.

There are better ways of projecting yourself than with showers of bumph.

Don't be put off by management-speak gobbledygook, but be inspired by it if you have to.

Bet your bottom dollar that something will always come along to ruin the best-laid plans of mice and men.

Chapter 12

When commercial expediency suppresses long term quality considerations, a credible challenge (however pointless) needs to be called from time to time.

If you want the easy life, go and work in the public services and be answerable to no-one.

At the risk of being repetitively boring, everyone ought to know that you cannot win a political argument with logic.

Try thanking God that there are people out in the wide world that make life such an interesting pastime for us ordinary mortals.

If the British cannot run a British brewing industry, what is it about foreigners that makes them think that *they* can? And they can. Surely it must have something to do with them not having to respond to the rigours, rules, influence, pressure and sometimes idiotic expectations of the British Stock Exchange and City?

Perhaps it is part of nature that as you advance towards a major lifestyle change like retirement, circumstances *automatically* arise that make you look forward to it.

Epilogue

Who was it who first said 'No situation is so dire that government interference cannot make it worse'?